BUILDING AND USING AN
ASTRONOMICAL OBSERVATORY

A beginner's guide to constructing a
telescope and setting up an observatory

BUILDING AND USING AN
ASTRONOMICAL OBSERVATORY

PAUL DOHERTY

Foreword by Patrick Moore

Patrick Stephens, Wellingborough

First published November 1986

British Library Cataloguing in Publication Data

Doherty, Paul
  Building and using an astronomical observatory.
  1. Telescope—Design and construction
  I. Title
  681'.412   QB88

  ISBN 0-85059-808-7

Patrick Stephens Limited is part of the Thorsons Publishing Group

Printed and bound in Great Britain.

Contents

Foreword

Do you want to have a telescope of your own, so that you can have detailed views of the craters of the Moon, the rings of Saturn and the satellites of Jupiter? Do you want to be able to see star-fields, coloured stars, star-clusters and the great dust-and-gas clouds which we call nebulæ? Many people would say 'Yes', but nowadays telescopes are very expensive. The alternative is to make your own, and in this book Paul Doherty shows you how to do it. Expertly, and with a deep knowledge of both telescopes and the objects to be observed, he guides you through the pitfalls — follow his advice, and you will be the proud possessor of a telescope which will serve you for a lifetime. This is a book which I recommend to you without reservation — and if you decide to try your hand, I wish you the very best of good fortune.

Patrick Moore
July 1986

Introduction

Nearly everyone at some time or other, has looked up at the stars and wondered what they really are. We are now in the fortunate position of knowing the answer to that question, thanks to the science of astronomy. The major tool in that science has been, and still is, the telescope. Most people still do not realize just what can be seen even with the most moderate sized telescope. This book, however, is written for those people who are not satisfied by these instruments, but wish to obtain a good astronomical telescope easily with little cost. It also contains information to help those who wish to take things further. It is possible that once the heavens have been viewed with a home-made telescope, many will wish to go on to set up their own observatory. Hopefully this book will help.

In Part One, the types of telescope there are, together with the various designs for a mount on which they can be fixed, are discussed and the readers are shown how to choose the type of combination that would best suit their needs. An understanding of the telescope, and just what it is meant to do, will help to ensure that time is spent only on those things that matter.

In Part Two a guide to the construction of a Newtonian reflector is given. This includes the making of the optical parts, right through to the construction of a mount. Rather than describe one type of mount, several are discussed together with various relevant details. The would-be telescope builder will be able to adapt the information to the construction of a small telescope or to one of quite moderate size. The book aims to be easy to follow for those who need a step by step guide, but the idea is not to give rigid guidelines so much as information which is adaptable so that those with imagination can build upon it. It relies heavily on the ability to make do with items of scrap material, and tells how to make that scrap into an attractive looking piece of scientific equipment.

For those who choose a fixed or semi-portable telescope, some sort of protective housing is desirable. This can be outstanding in its simplicity or quite adventurous. For this reason the details of more than one type are given, ranging from a simple run off shed to a proper domed observatory. Here, once more, it is not the intention to give a blow by blow, bolt by bolt account of how to build such housings—it is assumed that readers know how to fasten bolts and saw wood—the aim is to give ideas on which to expand.

Part Three explains how to use the telescope once you have constructed it, and how your observations can be of value to professional astronomical research.

Acknowledgements

There are many people who have been of assistance in the gathering of information for this book. I would particularly like to thank Stan Hewitt for kindly allowing me to use photographs and plans of his observatory in Stoke; Norman Oldham for allowing me to photograph his home-made 6 in reflector, and for his help together with Barry Pemberton of Orion Optics—their assistance in the optical portion of the book has been invaluable; Rick Wickham for allowing me to photograph and see plans of his home-made Dobsonian together with further advice on mirror construction and testing; Patrick Moore and Reg Spry for their permission to scrutinize and photograph their various observatories and telescopes; Alan Heath and John Mason for allowing use of photographs of their equipment.

Finally I would like to thank Bruce Quarrie for his encouragement and my wife Linda together with Gwen and Robert Gater for their help with the checking of the manuscript. Any mistakes are mine, not theirs.

Paul Doherty
Stoke on Trent, October 1985

Part One

Chapter 1

The history of the telescope

Most people when they hear the word telescope mentioned, think of a long tube which extends out for use, having a large lens at one end and a small lens at the other. Something of the sort Nelson put to his blind eye. This type of telescope does still exist, but the type we will be concerned with for an astronomical observatory is very different. Before we look at the various types of instrument around today, let us look at their history and development.

The very first telescope was invented in 1608 by a Dutchman from the Isle of Walcheren, named Hans Lippershey. He was a spectacle maker by trade and on announcing his discovery he stated that he had invented an instrument with which he could see a great distance. The story passed down through the years says that Lippershey's children had been playing with some of his spectacle lenses and, by chance alignment of two certain types, had suddenly seen a distant church steeple as though it were very much closer to them. Excitedly they ran and told their father about it, and on following this up Lippershey found that by placing two of the lenses a foot or so apart the steeple did indeed look much closer, furthermore, detail which he could not see without the lenses now became apparent. Realizing the importance of this discovery he continued to experiment, eventually producing a telescope proper by placing the lenses into a large tube. It is even recorded that he made a pair of binoculars.

Word of the invention spread and eventually came to the notice of Galileo Galilei of Padua University, while paying a visit to Venice. As Lippershey had realized its significance from a terrestrial point of view, Galileo saw its importance as an instrument for studying the heavens. He set about making one for himself, trying out different lenses. Galileo described his first attempt as two glass lenses fitted at each end of a lead tube, one of the glasses was flat on one side and spherically convex on the other. The second lens was flat on one side and concave on the other. He placed his eye against the concave lens. According to his records, this instrument magnified nine times (9×). After further experiments he finally ended up with an instrument which magnified 30×.

Galileo's first successful observations followed in 1609 and 1610. Through

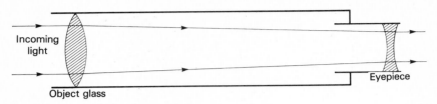

Figure 1. The Galilean telescope principle.

the years that followed he made many astounding discoveries. He saw craters and mountains on the Moon. He found that the planets showed discs, unlike the stars which always remained as pinpoints regardless of magnification. Venus and Mars also showed phases like the Moon, with Venus going through the full range, while Mars never showed less than the three-quarter phase. Jupiter was attended by four smaller bodies and to this day his discovery of them is commemorated by our referring to them as the Galilean satellites. He saw that the Milky Way could be resolved into countless stars and noted that the Sun was not a perfect object but occasionally showed dark spots on its brilliant face.

Possibly the most perplexing of Galileo's observations were those he made of Saturn. He noticed something very odd about its shape which seemed somehow to change from year to year. Sometimes it would be attended by two lesser spheres, whose positions, relative to the larger one, remained constant, unlike the smaller bodies attending Jupiter. In the following year they vanished, only to reappear two years later. Sometimes these smaller bodies looked as though they were attached to the main one. He could not understand the reason for the phenomena he was seeing, and died without ever learning of it.

Galileo suffered greatly for his observations and ideas, which tended to disprove the idea of the Earth-centred system and this did not please the church of the time. It was claimed that his 'optik tube' was bewitched, as were all those tricked into looking through it. He was eventually forced to say his observations and ideas were incorrect. He died in 1642, unhappy and nearly blind, which was possibly a result of his looking at the sun. The truth, however, would not die with him.

During the seventeenth century many great men followed in Galileo's footsteps. They began to make bigger and better telescopes. Most notable was Dutch astronomer Christian Huygens who developed a double element eyepiece still in use today and called the Huyghenian. With his telescope he made observations of markings on Mars and discovered Saturn's largest moon, Titan, in 1655. It was also he who realized the true nature of the rings of Saturn, solving the problem which so perplexed Galileo fifty years earlier.

Also busy were Giovanni Domenico Cassini, an Italian, and Johannes

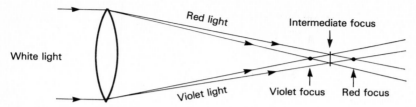

Figure 2. Chromatic aberration.

Hevelius of Danzig. Cassini built a telescope for the Paris observatory and actually observed a feature in the rings of Saturn, known now as the Cassini division. He also discovered four further satellites of Saturn. Hevelius produced one of the first good maps of the moon.

Gradually it became obvious that there were tremendous problems with the telescopes of the day, the main one being chromatic aberration. This was caused by light of different wavelengths being refracted to different degrees by the lenses. White light is made up of the various colours of the spectrum and these are not all brought to the same point of focus, the result is spurious prismatic colours which fringe the objects under view.

Later astronomers found that they were able to combat this problem to some extent by making telescopes of longer and longer focal length, and the telescopes of Cassini, Huygens and Hevelius were monstrous contraptions. Cassini had a lens suspended from a tower and attached to an ·eyepiece by a long pole. The telescope constructed by Huygens was an aerial type suspended by wires from a huge tower, and believed to be all of 200 ft (61 m) in length. Hevelius had a more modest instrument of only 150 ft (46 m) but records do suggest that telescopes were constructed which were probably three times this length, resembling huge ship's masts complete with rigging. Eventually it was realized that the development of these early refractors had been taken to the limit and they fell from favour. In fact it was to be another century before refractors were further improved.

In the meanwhile another type of telescope was invented. Originally the idea was suggested by a Scottish optician named James Gregory. His idea was to use a concave objective mirror which would form an image by reflection, instead of a lens which forms its image by refraction. The Gregorian reflector, as it became known, was never taken beyond an idea at that time but a reflecting telescope of another type was invented and built by none other than Isaac Newton in 1668. So credit for the reflector goes to him.

In the beginning Newton's reflector had only a 1 in aperture but it had great possibilities. It is still the most popular telescope for the amateur. Like Gregory's design, it also uses a concave primary mirror which sits at the bottom of the telescope tube. Incoming light hits the mirror and is reflected back up the tube to a point of focus. Before this point the converging light rays are intercepted by a second mirror which is set to deflect the rays at 90°

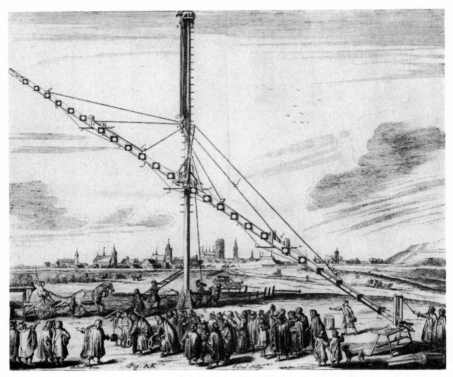

Figure 3. The aerial refractor constructed by Hevelius at Danzig. (Science Museum, London.)

to their original path. They then pass through a hole in the side of the tube where they can be examined with a normal eyepiece.

Because of this instrument's simplicity and ease of construction, telescopes with larger apertures could now be made which were short and free from chromatic aberration; this ousted the refractor for the best part of a century. By 1720 John Hadley in England had constructed a reflector of 6 in (150 mm) aperture, much larger than any refractor and instead of the inconvenient length of the aerial telescopes this was but 6 ft (183 cm) long.

The early reflectors did not use glass, they used speculum metal which was cheap, relatively easy to cast and could be polished to give excellent reflectivity. The major problem was that after a period of use the metal tarnished, having to be repolished. Though inconvenient it was considered a small price to pay for the excellence of the image that this new design afforded.

A further development for the reflector came in 1672, when G. Cassegrain of France came up with a design not unlike Gregory's. Cassegrain used a convex secondary, which instead of deflecting the light through the side of the tube sent it back down the tube through a hole in the centre of the primary mirror. Because of the shape of the secondary the focal length of the system is made greater than the Newtonian, but the telescope is on the whole shorter than a Newtonian of similar aperture. This design can probably be considered the most successful reflector design. It is used today in most major professional observatories.

Though out of the running for so long the refractor was far from dead. In the latter half of the eighteenth century it was once more set for a revival. Chester Moor Hall of England carried out experiments to find out what caused chromatic aberration and how to combat it. He finally managed to solve the problem by constructing an object glass that had two elements made of different types of glass. One was of crown, the other flint. By careful construction, chromatic aberration produced by the front element was countered by the back element because the two materials have different refractive properties. There were still problems, however. Firstly, because of difficulties in casting optical glass discs, the refractor aperture remained small, at around 2¼ in (60 mm) and secondly because Hall did not make his findings public.

Figure 4. Replica of Newton's reflecting telescope. (Science Museum, London.)

By this time reflectors had become really popular. Mirrors of particular excellence were being produced by James Short around 1735 and he was now making successful Gregorian instruments of up to 20 in aperture (50 cm).

The refractor had another burst of popularity in 1755, when John Dollond, independently of Hall, succeeded in producing an achromatic doublet. He had the sense to make and sell his instruments. There was still the problem of aperture and even though small, Dollond's instruments were very expensive. So, though they looked set to make their mark, they once again lost favour. Glassmakers could not cast discs of greater aperture than 3 in (76 mm) while reflectors were being constructed of larger and larger aperture.

The continued popularity of the reflector was due mainly to a great astronomer named William Herschel. He had taken an interest in astronomy quite late in life, at the age of 35. His career was in music, but his newly acquired love of astronomy was soon to take over his life completely. He decided to construct his own reflecting telescopes, becoming very good at this indeed. In 1781, while making routine observations with one of his 7 ft telescopes of 6 in (152 mm) aperture, he chanced upon a discovery that was to change his life. Many have been unkind enough to say that his discovery was luck, it was not. The truth is that Herschel's telescopes were so good, and his observing skill equally so, that he noticed that one particular star, picked up during an observing session on 13 March, looked different from the normal stars and he made a particular note of it. At first he thought the small fuzzy bluish green disc was a comet. It turned out to be a major planet, now called Uranus, and the first such object ever to be discovered in this way. All the other planets had been known since the dawn of history.

The discovery changed Herschel's life. He was later to receive a royal grant which enabled him to devote his life to astronomy and to the building of larger reflecting telescopes. His largest creation had a 48 in (122 cm) mirror and a length of 40 ft (12 m) which he completed in 1789. Herschel made many discoveries with his self-built telescopes, among which were the addition of two satellites to his own planet, Uranus, and two additional satellites of Saturn.

The mirrors in Herschel's telescopes were still of speculum metal, which he experimented with to the point of being able to cast the 48 in disc. The largest instrument was rather cumbersome in design and difficult to handle. It was suspended by a massive framework needing other people to manoeuvre it while Herschel made his observations. The increase of light grasp with the 48 in lens was enormous, but because of the nature of the metal mirror it tarnished quickly and repolishing a speculum of this size was, of course, a major task. This, plus the difficulty in handling, forced Herschel to use one of his smaller telescopes, though it was still 20 ft (6 m) long, and had an 18 in (457 mm) mirror. This became Herschel's favourite and he made many remarkable observations with it.

Figure 5. An engraving of Herschel's 40 ft (12 m) reflector. The telescope was the largest of its time, having an aperture of 48 in (122 cm). It required assistants to move it while in use. Herschel used the instrument as a front view or Herschelian telescope. It was originally sited at Observatory House in Slough. (Royal Astronomical Society.)

The excellence of Herschel's mirrors was underlined when he had the opportunity to view through a 9½ in (241 mm) telescope made by another well-respected mirror maker of the time named Short. Compared with his own, Short's instrument was poor. Herschel decided, on the strength of this, to manufacture and sell his own reflectors. He became as well known for this as he did for his observational work.

An interesting variation of the reflector that Herschel used was to do away with the secondary mirror and view from the front of the telescope. Speculum metal is not a particularly highly reflective material and doing away with this second mirror increased light grasp considerably, since it reduced the number of reflecting surfaces in the system from two to one. The problem of course is that if the mirror sits squarely at the bottom of the tube, the image is formed in an inaccessible position centrally placed in the tube. To view it an observer would need to place their head in front of the telescope thus blocking off incoming light, losing the advantage of the removal of the secondary. Herschel hit on the idea of tilting the primary mirror slightly so that the converging cone of light was reflected to an eye-

Figure 6. *The principle of the front view or Herschelian reflector.*

piece fixed at the upper end lip of the tube. This form of telescope, known as the front view or Herschelian, has now fallen into disuse. Tilting the mirror in this way produces astigmatic distortion of the image. Herschel got away with it only because the ratio of focal length to aperture was so large that this distortion was not so obvious.

Herschel's 48 in (122 cm) remained the world's largest telescope for over half a century. However the thirst for larger aperture telescopes felt by Herschel was also felt by others. In 1845 William Parsons, the third Earl of Rosse, built a gigantic reflector with a mirror 6 ft (180 cm) across and a focal length of 60 ft (18 m). So large was the tube that he decided to mount it between two huge thick walls in his grounds at Birr Castle in Parsonstown, Ireland. Because of its size and construction the 'Leviathan', as it became known, was very restricted in its movement, being mainly up and down with little lateral movement—rather like a huge transit instrument. This meant that the Earl could not swing his telescope to any part of the sky he wished, instead he had to wait until diurnal rotation brought a particular object he wanted to view to a part of the sky that was accessible to him.

Despite these difficulties the amazing light grasp of the telescope enabled him to detect the spiral structure of certain faint nebulae, which we now know to be spiral galaxies. But it was certainly inconvenient and once more telescopes had advanced beyond the capabilities of the technology of the time. The type of movement of the telescope was inadequate and speculum metal tarnished quickly. The need for regular polishing became a major task with mirrors so large. Also with a metal disc of this size distortions and aberrations became objectionable. Had the reflector finally reached its peak?

At first the refractor seemed to offer no alternative. It remained virtually impossible to cast flint glass discs that were perfectly flawless. Refractors of 2-3 in (50-76 mm) were the largest possible. But, at the time when reflectors began to meet with major problems, experiments with casting refractor objectives began to make some headway. Even during the time of Herschel some major advances were being made. This was thanks to the work of a Swiss optician, Pierre Guinard. After many years' work Guinard began to produce high quality glass discs, ranging from 4-6 in (101-152 mm) and even

8 in (202 mm) diameter. All that remained was for someone to work these discs and turn them into precision lenses. This was done by Joseph von Fraunhöfer of Munich. Due to the work of these two, the refractor was once more in the running.

Fraunhöfer's design was slightly different to Dolland's, though the flint/crown combination was still used. The end result of their combined work was the magnificent 9½ in (241 mm) objective of the great Dorpat refractor, completed in 1824. Not only did Fraunhöfer make the objective for this instrument, he also devised a mount for it which has since become known as the German equatorial, a mount still used for refractors and reflectors to this day.

Though still not achieving the apertures of the giant reflectors, the excellence of the design and quality of the optics made the refractor a very worthy instrument, sought after by major observatories. Fraunhöfer refractors became universally recognized for their worth, especially in the measurement of double stars and parallax. Here size for size, in my view, the refractor leaves the reflector standing, though some would disagree on this point.

For 23 years the Dorpat refractor remained the largest instrument of its type in the world. Most impressive though is the work that was able to be carried out with it. The field was now open for larger and larger refractors, but progress remained slow. In 1847 a 14 in (360 mm) refractor was installed at the Harvard College observatory by the German firm, Merz and Mahler. It was with this instrument that W. C. and G. P. Bond discovered Saturn's dusky inner ring, known as the Crepe ring or ring C.

Refractors were soon to reach their limit of perfection and this was to be achieved by an American named Alvan Clark. Clark had been interested by his son George, who had been attempting to make a mirror. With Alvan's help the mirror was duly completed, but they were very disappointed with the way it soon tarnished, needing further polishing. Alvan was unimpressed with the temporary nature of this well-figured metal mirror, so he began to experiment with object glasses. Soon he was producing lenses of supreme quality.

Their fame spread quickly and in 1862 the firm of Alvan Clark and Son completed an object glass of 18½ in (457 mm) aperture. They then went on to make many fine lenses of all sizes but among their most famous must be the 26 in (71 cm) made for the Naval observatory in Washington, the 36 in (91 cm) for Lick observatory and the 40 in (101 cm) for the Yerkes observatory, Chicago. This latter refractor is to this day the largest in the world and still of major importance to astronomy, even though completed in 1897, as indeed are the 26 in and the 36 in refractors.

Other companies also took on the work of making large refractors and the names of Merz and Grubb were to figure highly. With the completion of the Yerkes 40 in (101 cm) refractor it seems, finally, that this type of instrument has reached its limit. The problems become enormous and insurmountable. The sheer weight of the glass causes it to sag. There can of course be no

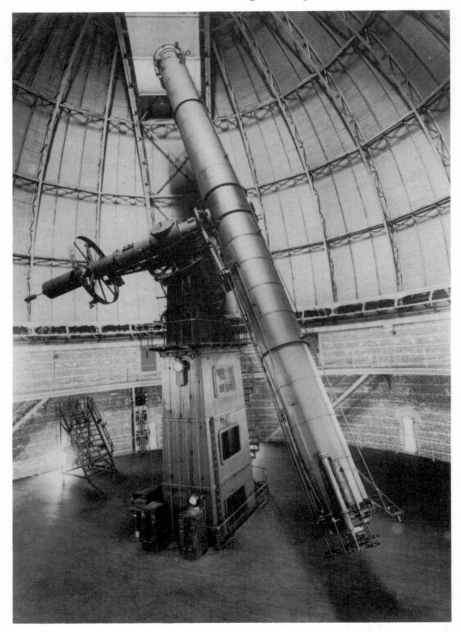

Figure 7. The Yerkes 40 in (101 cm) refractor. (Royal Astronomical Society.)

support as the aperture has to remain unobstructed. As the glass flexes under its own weight the lens curvature is deformed and the performance is impaired.

So, even though refractors had stolen the limelight in the latter half of the nineteenth century, reflector development did not stop. In 1856, shortly after the building of the Rosse 72 in (180 cm), Carl von Steinheil of Germany, together with Léon Foucault, suggested and produced a mirror made of glass. It would be highly polished and permanent in nature. It could have a silver coating deposited upon it chemically to render it highly reflective, and when tarnished this coating could be removed and replaced without any detriment to the figure of the mirror itself. The glass did not need to be of the high quality required for refractor lenses, so costing less. The silver would be applied to its front surface and no light would pass through the glass itself. Furthermore flexure would not be so much of a problem because the glass could be well supported from behind. The development was highly successful and soon a reflector of 36 in (91 cm) aperture was constructed by an Englishman named A. A. Common, together with Alvan Clark, which was a first class instrument. Later in 1891 Common attempted a 60 in (150 cm) reflector, though this was not so successful.

Because of the problems experienced with large refractors, and their enormous cost, reflectors took over once more for the last time. To the present day this is how the situation has remained.

The cost of the Yerkes observatory and telescope was very high indeed. It was to a large extent paid for by a millionaire businessman Charles Tyson Yerkes, who made his money while in charge of the Chicago Trolley system. He was talked into parting with almost $350,000 by George Ellery Hale who, it was to turn out, had a gift for doing this sort of thing. Hale was to apply this gift to the setting up of another observatory at Mount Wilson. His father had obtained a 60 in (150 cm) glass blank at a cost of $25,000. Originally it was intended for the Yerkes observatory, but never installed due to lack of funds. George Hale once again managed to find finance, this time from the Carnegie Foundation. The Mount Wilson observatory was set up at a site which satisfied him.

Though the site may have been good enough for Hale it was not long before he was looking to build a larger telescope. In fact he was looking for cash for this while the 60 in was still under construction. He found his fresh source of funds in the person of J. D. Hooker, a businessman who desperately wanted to have his name given to the world's largest telescope. $45,000 was given toward the building of an 84 in (2.1 m) telescope. It appears, though, that Hale probably pointed out that such a telescope would not be the world's largest for long, because Hooker increased his contribution so that a telescope of 100 in (2.5 m) aperture became possible. This was finally completed in 1918 and was to remain the world's largest telescope for thirty years.

Many discoveries have been made with this instrument which have been of great importance. With them came the realization that our galaxy is not the universe itself but one of many such star systems spread throughout a greater universe than we could ever have imagined. Some of these galaxies were the spiral nebulae seen by Rosse with his giant reflector. The decision to close the 100 in telescope in 1985 came as a great shock to astronomers the world over.

Hale, however, had not stopped there. Despite poor health he began his fund raising activities again, with the aim to build a 200 in (500 cm) or 300 in (750 cm) reflector, settling for the former as the more practical project. Because of the increasing light pollution around Mount Wilson a new site was chosen, this time at Mount Palomar, California. There were great problems experienced in the casting of such a large disc. It was decided that Pyrex would be used because of its low expansion properties. To keep the weight of this enormous mirror down, a system of ribbing was moulded into the mirror, allowing cavities to cut down on the amount of glass. The first casting went very wrong. When the molten glass was poured into the moulding some of the cores, which would form the cavities, broke off and became embedded in the glass. When tested it was found that strains in the disc had resulted.

A second casting was made and this time it was successful. It took nearly eleven months to cool, while in the grinding and polishing that followed no less than five tons of glass were removed. The mirror was to have a hole so that it could be used at the Cassegrain focus as well as at the prime focus. An idea of the size of the mirror can be gained from the fact that this hole is 40 in (101 cm) across, as large as the world's biggest refractor lens.

Unfortunately Hale did not live to see the telescope finished, he died in 1938. The completion of the telescope was delayed by the Second World War and it was not used until January 1948. It was dedicated five months later and named the Hale Telescope after the man whose vision and drive had made it possible.

Now at last we are at the limit of size for Earth-based reflector telescopes. The Russians have a larger 236 in (600 cm) reflector now, but it is difficult to establish just how successful this has been. There are now many other giant reflectors throughout the world with sizes ranging from 120 in (300 cm) to 158 in (400 cm). Though, at the moment, we have probably reached the size limit, technology has enabled us to concentrate on improvement within this limit and though inferior in size the new reflectors are of superior quality. This is not meant as a criticism of the 200 in, a measure of just how good this telescope is must be found in the fact that it was with it that Halley's Comet was first located, on its 1985/86 return. It was picked up on 16 October 1982 when still way beyond the orbit of Saturn, and an amazing seven million times fainter than the Pole star. New electronic equipment was used in conjunction with the telescope and this adaptability must mean that it is still one of, if not the major optical instrument in astronomy today.

The modern reflectors of today will probably be bettered in both size and

Figure 8. The 200 in (500 cm) Hale Telescope at Mount Palomar. (Hale Observatories.)

design. New ideas will always come along. For the moment, though, the only way that can be seen for them to develop further will be to send telescopes into space, away from our atmosphere and beyond the effect of gravity. Greater sizes will then be possible because in the absence of gravity, flexure will no longer be a problem. Mirror coatings should last indefinitely away from all forms of pollution. So we must now look to space for the next major development of the telescope.

Chapter 2

Lens forms

There are many different lens types which you may come into contact with and which you will read about in this book. Figure 9 shows the various forms so that when you do encounter them you will have an idea of what you are dealing with.

There are occasions when it becomes necessary to take lenses or eyepieces apart. This is a practice I do not recommend unless it is vital, such as for cleaning or replacement of cement. If the lens surfaces are identical on both faces, then it will not matter which way round that lens is used, it will act the same way. More often than not, however, the surfaces are not identical and it matters very much which way round the lens is positioned. If there are a number of elements concerned then it becomes very easy to mix them up, in fact, I would go so far as to say that if certain steps are not taken it is impossible not to mix them up. Lens forms are not always obvious and it is often difficult to discern the form of the lens surfaces, especially if the difference is only slight. Therefore, before splitting the components of a lens, always mark the edge of the combined lens in such a way that will

Figure 9. Different lens forms; (a) Plano convex, (b) Plano concave, (c) Equi convex, (d) Equi concave, (e) positive Meniscus, (f) negative Meniscus, (g) Crossed Bi convex, (h) Crossed Bi concave.

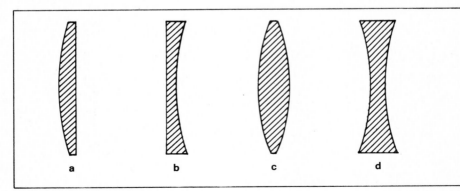

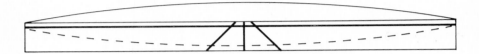

Figure 10. How to mark lenses to ensure correct reassembly should it be found necessary to separate components. Always mark with pencil in the way shown, with the arrow pointing to the front face.

indicate their front surfaces and the order in which they fit together. This is quite easy and should be done as shown in Figure 10.

In this way the arrow points to the lens front. By aligning it, the lenses will be back in their original position. It is easy to do, but just as easy to forget. By forgetting, a great deal of trouble will certainly be caused. If it sounds as though I am speaking from experience, I am!

So far as the way the lens acts, basically the stronger the curvature of the lens the greater the deviation of the light rays. Therefore, the rays will be brought to a focus closer to the back surface of the lens. The more gentle the curve the less the deviation of the rays so the focal point will be at a greater distance from the back surface.

The image formed by a lens of shorter focus will not be of such a large scale as an image formed by a lens of longer focus. This image, formed by the lens, can then be examined as if it were a real object by looking at it through a second lens, made specially, and called an ocular or eyepiece. This in essence is a telescope.

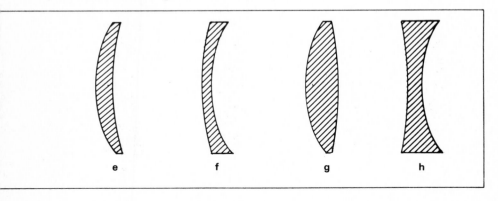

Chapter 3

Types of telescope

In the following list of telescope types an idea will be given of the simplicity or complexity of a particular design, together with their advantages or disadvantages. Telescopes used in astronomy are of the simplest type, far simpler than those used for terrestrial purposes. With a terrestrial telescope the image seen through it has to be erect. To accommodate this there have to be a large number of lenses in the system. The more glass there is the greater the light loss through absorption, the more lens surfaces there are the more light will be lost, again, through reflection.

In astronomy our main concern is to collect as much light as we can so as few lenses as possible are used. The result is that the image appears inverted, annoying if used for terrestrial purposes but mattering not a jot in astronomical viewing. All astronomical charts of the moon and planets are drawn with south at the top, the main exception being charts or photographs from space probes. In this case just turn them upside down if you wish to compare them with your view through the telescope. All of this of course applies only to northern hemisphere observers. Observers in the southern hemisphere see things in the sky the opposite way up anyway. So you see, in astronomy it really doesn't matter.

Let us look at the various telescope types you are most likely to encounter and perhaps this will aid you in choosing which is the best type to suit your needs.

The refractor
The telescope design has a large clear lens or objective at the front end of the telescope, which refracts the light bringing it to a focus some distance behind the lens, where the image formed is examined with an eyepiece.

If only a single lens objective is used then chromatic aberration becomes a considerable problem. By constructing an objective with two or more elements which have different optical properties and by careful design this problem can be countered to a large extent, and the light rays forced to focus at nearly the same point. Despite this, refractors still tend to be plagued by spurious colour and observations concerning colour can never be entirely trusted.

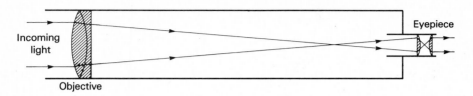

Figure 11. The principle of the refractor.

Because of the need for special glass and the need to perfect a number of optical surfaces in multiple-element objectives the cost is very high even for a small diameter. Also refractors tend to have long focal lengths, their focal ratio (ratio of focal length to objective diameter) being f13 to f15 or even f20 so, even for a telescope with small aperture, the instrument is long and needs a large housing.

The image seen through a good refractor is far superior to that seen with a reflector of similar aperture. Star images appear sharper because of the absence of a central obstruction, like the secondary of a reflector. Useful work can be done with quite moderate apertures and a 5-6 in (127-152 mm) is a very worthwhile instrument to have. Though the construction of a refractor telescope is quite simple, to make an objective lens is not, considerable skill being required. Very few amateurs attempt them and it is very unusual to find sizeable ones in amateur hands.

Reflectors
The Newtonian
As already described this type of telescope uses a silvered, concave, paraboloid mirror and a smaller, flat surfaced, secondary. It is completely free from chromatic aberration. Because the glass for the mirrors does not need to be of superior quality, large diameter mirrors can be obtained quite

Figure 12. The principle of the Newtonian reflector.

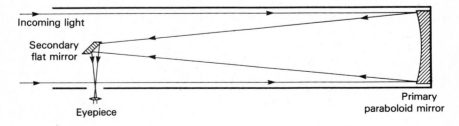

cheaply. Big reflectors have superior light grasp against refractors with the same aperture because there is no loss through absorption. The Newtonian is much shorter than refractors of similar aperture and is therefore much easier to mount. Useful f ratios are between f4 and f10. Because of the position of the eyepiece they are easy to use, though this can become difficult if of greater size.

There are disadvantages with the Newtonian. It suffers from tube currents which do not trouble the closed in tube of the refractor. There are diffraction effects which are caused by the central obstruction (secondary and mount). It is also necessary to re-align the optical parts every so often, again something one rarely has to do with a refractor. Finally the mirror coating does deteriorate with time, occasionally needing replacement, as with most reflectors.

Despite these disadvantages, which are all minor, the attributes of the Newtonian are so considerable that it is the most popular telescope for the amateur.

The Cassegrain
In this system a concave paraboloid primary is again used but, instead of the elliptical flat of the Newtonian, a convex hyperboloid secondary mirror is used. This reflects the light directly back down the tube through a hole in the primary. The shape of the secondary alters the angle of convergence of the light rays from the primary, so effectively increasing the focal length of the system. In this way focal ratios similar to the refractor can be achieved but, by the use of a short focal ratio primary, the overall length of the system is kept short.

The long focal ratio possible leads to some advantages. A larger image scale is achieved, coma is reduced and spherical aberration all but non-existent. Basically the Cassegrain combines many of the advantages of a Newtonian reflector and a refractor.

The disadvantages are greater than with the Newtonian. The telescope has a small field which tends to be curved and astigmatic. Because of the need for a large secondary, diffraction effects can be considerable. It is

Figure 13. The principle of the Cassegrain reflector.

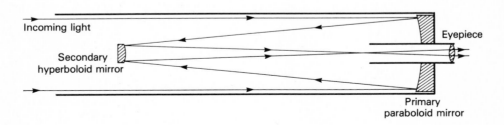

rather more expensive than the Newtonian and, from an amateur point of view, the need to figure a convex secondary and make a primary with a hole, presents certain problems. One problem is that the eyepiece is sometimes found in inconvenient positions and this can be made worse by a poor choice of mount. Fork type mounts are not ideal. Also, since one is viewing from behind the mirror, body heat tends to cause air turbulence around the mirror making for poor seeing. Alignment of the optical parts can be a little tricky, also image contrast is somewhat reduced through light from the sky falling directly on to it. This can be cut down by the addition of a length of tube which should protrude, some way up into the main tube, from the hole in the primary mirror.

The design is quite popular, however, and widely used by both amateurs and professionals, many are of the opinion that it is not appreciated by the amateur as much as it should be. I personally feel that with the difficulties of construction, when compared to the Newtonian, it is not likely to become as popular.

* * *

These are the most common instruments to be found in amateur hands. Lately more adventurous amateurs have obtained, and built, more specialized and sophisticated instruments for specific purposes and, though less common, they will now be found in increasing numbers.

Schmidt camera
Designed by Bernhard Schmidt in 1930. It uses a concave spheroidal mirror. Located at this mirror's centre of curvature is a lens-like corrector plate. This element has a flat rear surface but a front surface with a complex shape. Its purpose is to allow a large field of view with good definition out to its edge. The field itself is focused on to a spherical surface so photographic plates used with this system have to be curved to match this. The diameter of the mirror is greater than that of the corrector plate. Very short focal lengths are possible, eg f1, and this results in a fast photographic system.

Figure 14. The principle of the Schmidt camera.

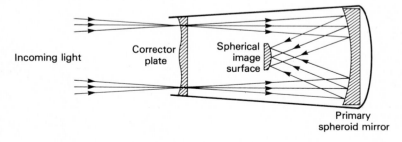

Incoming light   Corrector plate   Spherical image surface   Primary spheroid mirror

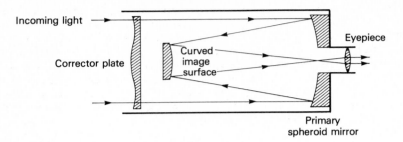

Figure 15. The principle of the Schmidt Cassegrain.

Ordinary reflector telescopes have a limited field of view. The best large reflectors are only good for up to 1° due to image quality deterioration with increasing distance from the optical axis. Schmidt cameras do not suffer in this way, an average field of view can be 4-5°.

Schmidt Cassegrain
A further application of the Schmidt design, which can be used both as a photographic and visual instrument having a flatter, larger field than normal reflectors. It is astigmatism and coma free but it requires the figuring of two mirrors and a corrector plate, which renders the type rather expensive.

Maksutov
This system has a fairly thick spherical meniscus lens and concave spherical primary mirror. Figure 16 shows a Cassegrain-type Maksutov. Here all surfaces in the system are spherical. The secondary in this type needs only to be an aluminized patch on the centre of the rear surface of the corrector lens. This means there is no secondary spider mount and no resulting diffraction problem, except from the central obstruction itself.

Figure 16. The principle of the Maksutov.

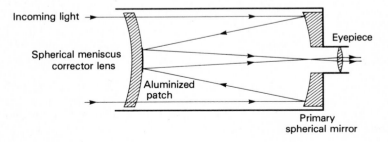

With this instrument a wide field of view is obtained. By the use of a small f ratio primary and by placing the corrector inside the focal point of this primary, the telescope is very compact. The Maksutov is as near a perfect instrument as one can get. The reason these types of telescope have not been used as the giant instruments of major observatories is, simply, due to the same problems that large refractors face. The corrector lens is an unsupported element and thus flexes under its own weight, limiting its size. It is virtually free from aberration and astigmatism. A brilliant wide flat field is obtained and the total length of the instrument need only be around one fifth of the instrument's focal length.

The Maksutov has now become a popular commercial instrument, though it is quite expensive. Home-made instruments do exist but difficulties in the making of the corrector lens stems its popularity in this direction.

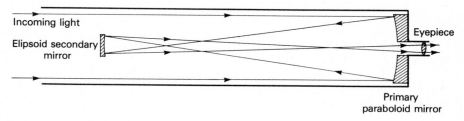

Figure 17. The principle of the Gregorian reflector.

Gregorian

This instrument is no longer made but it is likely to be encountered, since it was a popular instrument many years ago. It will be found in the possession of those who own it for its historical interest or antique value. It is worthy of description though because of its history.

It is not unlike the Cassegrain in basic form though it is longer and uses a concave ellipsoid secondary. The eyepiece is positioned behind the mirror as with a Cassegrain, the light rays passing through a hole in the primary. Originally focus was achieved by moving the secondary and not the eyepiece. Unlike other types of astronomical telescope the image is the correct way up.

* * *

From reading these brief descriptions an idea may be obtained as to which instrument you should choose. If cost is not your prime concern and photography your aim, then the Schmidt would be the best choice. If perfection of view is of interest but not considerable aperture, then the Schmidt Cassegrain or Maksutov would suit; these will also act as good photographic instruments. For convenience, relative cheapness and ease of construction the Newtonian reflector must take the lead. In the section on telescope construction, the basic steps for making such an instrument are given in detail.

For a home observatory the equipment need not be limited to one type of telescope. It is advisable to familiarize yourself with them all. Small refractors, for instance, are excellent as finders or guide telescopes for your main instruments. You may find the need to construct one, even if you purchase the lens.

Chapter 4

Telescope function

Before you can consider purchasing or making a telescope for your observatory it is rather important to learn a few facts about how it works and what
are the most important factors. Just what can you expect from a telescope?

There are many complex forms of telescope but in astronomy we are
initially concerned with the simplest. All other forms or designs are derived
from it and so far as the basic principles are concerned these are best
explained by use of this type. There are several functions it must perform.
Each is important in its own right and often one depends on another to be
effective.

Light grasp

Nowhere is this more important than with telescopes used in astronomy. In
most cases the objects we are looking at are dim so as much of their light as
possible needs to be collected. We can then examine them with comparative
ease.

The light grasp of a telescope is the amount of light, from a given source,
that the objective is able to concentrate in forming the image at its focal
point. This is dependent on the diameter of the objective. It is nothing to do
with magnification or the objective's focal length. Put another way, the
objective of a telescope is regarded as a collector. The retina can only receive
in as much light as is allowed through by the pupil. Light, from a given
source in space, is falling on to the whole of the Earth's hemisphere directed
toward it. At night the pupil of the eye opens to a diameter of just over ¼ in
(7 mm) and the retina will be excited only by the amount of light passing
through this aperture, which has an area of about $1^1/_{10}$ sq in (28 sq mm).

Now, if the objective of the telescope has a diameter of 6 in (152 mm) then
all of the light falling on to its surface will be concentrated into the image.
The retina will accordingly be excited by this, having the benefit, in effect, of
a pupil of 6 in diameter and a surface area 466 times greater, at 28 sq in (177 sq
cm). This is of course in theory. In practice not all of the light falling on to the
objective is reflected or transmitted. There is always a loss through
absorption and reflection of lens surfaces or the poor reflectivity of mirror
surfaces. Generally this loss amounts to 35 per cent. However, this is the

principle and the obvious point is the bigger the objective, the more light is collected so the greater the light grasp. The brightness of an image then is proportional to the area of the objective. We will find that if we double the aperture we increase its light gathering power by four times.

The way in which we can judge this light grasp best is by assessing the magnitude of the faintest star a given instrument will show. There is a formula but it is too involved to give here. In any case there is disagreement on it since there are so many factors involved, such as atmospheric conditions, the individual's own personal thresholds, state of mirror surfaces, etc. Before we can appreciate the capability of various apertures we need to know a little about stellar brightness or magnitudes, as seen with the unaided eye, and the way the magnitude scale works.

Magnitude is a measure of the brightness of astronomical objects and a magnitude scale has been devised to describe the difference in the relative brightness of these various objects. There are certain standard stars which have been numbered first on this scale, these are the brighter ones. Each step in magnitude corresponds to a brightness ratio of 2.512 so a first magnitude star is around two and a half times brighter than a second magnitude star. The brighter the star is, the smaller its magnitude value.

The faintest stars that can be seen with the unaided eye, on a good night, are around magnitude 6 to 6.5. A star of magnitude 6 is one hundred times fainter than one of first magnitude. There are stars which are brighter than first magnitude, a star two and a half times brighter is magnitude 0 while one two and a half times brighter than 0 is − 1. The brightest star in the sky, Sirius, has a magnitude of − 1.4. The following table will give some idea of expected limiting magnitudes for certain apertures, though as already mentioned many factors are involved and the values given are only a guide.

Aperture		Refractor	Reflector
in	mm		
2	50	11.3	11.1
3	76	12.2	12.0
4	108	12.7	12.5
6	162	13.6	13.5
8	216	14.2	14.1
10	254	14.6	14.6
12	305	15.0	15.0

It must also be pointed out that the amount of magnification used will affect the values obtained. The range of limiting magnitudes using various magnifications with a 12 in (305 mm) can be expected to be as follows:

50×	100×	200×
13.4	14.2	14.9

(Devised by I. S. Bowen.)

All of this is dependent on sky conditions and the method employed in observing. For example, fainter stars can be detected if the eye is not directed straight at them. Averted vision, as it is called, is a useful trick when observing very faint objects. So effective is it that objects will easily be visible which are invisible when the eye is directed exactly toward them.

Telescope resolution

This is the ability of a telescope to see, as two separate objects, two point images which are close together. In theory this is limited by the telescope aperture. The larger the aperture, the greater the resolving power. So, as with light grasp, aperture is the major factor.

The main problem is due to diffraction, or the bending of light rays when they encounter an obstacle. This means that star images formed by a lens or mirror can never appear as perfect points. The image will consist of a small central disc (the Airy disc) which is brightest at the centre and which fades off towards the edge. This in turn is surrounded by a series of concentric rings, which themselves become fainter with increasing radius. These rings are comparatively faint and with most stars only the ring closest in is obvious, though with very bright stars more rings will be seen. The size of the discs depends on the telescope aperture. The larger the aperture the smaller the discs appear, and so the less likely close images are to overlap.

Resolution will of course be severely affected by atmospheric conditions and never is the theoretical resolving power of a given aperture achieved with Earth-based telescopes. It will be interesting to see if space telescopes reach this limit once placed beyond our atmosphere. The resolving power of a telescope will in no way be aided by increased magnification. All that will happen is the Airy discs will be enlarged. Close images will still overlap even though their centres are now further apart. All that can be done is to reduce the size of the spurious disc and this can only be done by increasing aperture.

During the nineteenth century, English amateur astronomer and observer of double stars, W. R. Dawes, found that there was a practical limit for the resolving power of given apertures, which could be measured in seconds of arc. The arc is a unit of measure used in astronomy. It is derived by taking a line around the whole celestial sphere and splitting it up into 360°. Each degree is split up into 60 minutes of arc and each minute into 60 seconds of arc. To give an idea of scale, the Moon is on average 30 arc minutes in apparent diameter or 1,800 arc seconds. At 40× the planet Jupiter presents a disc the same size as that which the Moon shows to the unaided eye. Its average apparent diameter is 45 arc seconds (45").

Dawes found that by using the constant 4.56 and dividing it by the size of the telescope aperture in inches, the resolving power of the telescope in arc seconds would be given. Put simply: $\frac{4.56}{1} = 4.56$. So a telescope with a 1 in (25 mm) aperture should have a resolving power of 4.56 arc seconds, while one of 10 in (254 mm) aperture will resolve .456 arc seconds.

This has become known as the Dawes limit, like many things it depends on certain factors. In the splitting of double stars it is assumed that each of the two stars has the same magnitude. It also assumes one is using optics that are of excellent quality.

Magnification

Generally the newcomer to the field of astronomy has the idea that magnification is the only important function of a telescope, in fact it is a belief among most laymen when thinking of telescopes. To say it is not important is silly, because there would be no point in a telescope with excellent light grasp and good resolution capabilities that were not used to enlarge the image. Compared with the two functions mentioned above, however, it is of secondary importance, though it depends entirely on each of those functions to be effective. Newcomers, to be fair to them, are not always guided from their ideas by telescope dealers many of whom use magnifying power as the major selling point. The result is that most small aperture telescopes are pushed hopelessly beyond their practical limits, yielding only poorly defined, fuzzy, dim images.

In a telescope both the objective and the eyepiece play their part in the magnification. By combining the two, with their own respective focal lengths, we achieve an overall magnification for the system. Both objective and ocular magnify in their own right, so we need to consider each separately.

The size of an image formed at the primary focus of an objective is a result of the focal length of that objective. The diameter will have no effect other than on the image brightness. Therefore it will be seen that a 2 in (50 mm) objective with a focal ratio of 15 (f15)—that is a 30 in (76 cm) focal length— will give the same image size at its primary focus as will a 6 in (152 mm) f5 objective; ie, 15×2 in $= 30$ in and 5×6 in $= 30$ in.

It happens that an objective on its own will magnify once for each 10 in (254 mm) of focal length. Therefore an objective which has a focal length ten times as long, or 100 in (250 cm), will give a prime focus image that is ten times larger than if the object were viewed with the unaided eye.

Now, what happens when we use an eyepiece? The same sort of relationship applies. An ocular with a focal length of 1 in (25 mm) will also magnify ten times. To illustrate this, place your finger 10 in away from one of your eyes, it will appear a certain size. That distance is recognized as a standard, least distance for good definition with a size regarded as though it were magnified once. The one inch focal length of the eyepiece is one tenth of this distance and it is like viewing the finger as though it were only one inch away, so it will appear ten times bigger.

If we use that eyepiece with the telescope of 100 in (250 cm) focal length and its resulting $10\times$ primary focus image, we are then enlarging that image a further ten times—$10 \times 10 = 100$. This is the overall magnification of the combination.

There is a limit to how high a magnification should be used with a given objective diameter. The ideal would be 25D to 30D, D being the diameter of the objective in inches. So a 10 in (254 mm) instrument should give its best at around 250× to 300×. The main reasons for this limit are the resolving power of the instrument, which as already mentioned cannot be improved by increased magnification, and the atmospheric conditions. It is sometimes possible to go higher, particularly with refractors. If one has superb seeing conditions and a first class lens then 50D might be possible. Some say even higher but frankly there is little to be gained. Image quality suffers and image brightness is reduced. I often use 320× with a 16½ in (419 mm) reflector which is only 20D. A bright sharp image is to be preferred even if a little smaller. The perfect compromise is 25 per inch of aperture, which conveniently converts to metric as 1× per mm of aperture.

Besides there being an upper limit to magnifications used there is also a lower limit below which it is useless to go. The reason is that the beam of light leaving the eyepiece and entering the eye varies in diameter with a change of magnification. The lower the magnification, the larger the beam or exit pupil. We eventually reach a point where the exit pupil is larger than the pupil of the eye. If this happens the iris of the eye is then an effective diaphragm, cutting down the brightness of the image so in effect cancelling out some of the benefit of having a large objective. Secondly, the larger the exit pupil the greater the area of eye lens used. If your eye suffers from any defect, such as astigmatism, then the more of its lens that is used the greater will be the trouble from the defect. For people with eye lens defects, the smaller the exit pupil the better. The lowest one should go is probably 5D. The formula for finding the diameter of the exit pupil is expressed thus:

$$E = \frac{D}{M} \; or \; \text{exit pupil} = \frac{\text{diameter of objective}}{\text{magnification}}$$

Let us say we are using a 6 in (152 mm) telescope with a power of 12×. Here the exit pupil will be ½ in (13 mm) which is twice as large as the average pupil diameter at night. Therefore, only a quarter of the light collected by the objective is passing through to the retina, so one might as well be using a 3 in (75 mm) reflector.

The following table gives maximum and minimum magnifications to be used with various apertures. Based on a ¼ in (7 mm) exit pupil and maximum magnifications of 25D and 30D.

Aperture		Minimum	Maximum	Maximum
in	mm	5D	25D	30D
3	76	15	75	90
4	101	20	100	120
5	127	25	125	150
6	152	30	150	180

Aperture		Minimum	Maximum	Maximum
in	mm	5D	25D	30D
8	203	40	200	240
10	254	50	250	300
12	305	60	300	360
15	381	75	375	450
18	457	90	450	540
24	609	120	600	720

I have decided on two maximum magnifications because though 25D is the ideal, I have often found 30D perfectly acceptable.

Real and apparent fields

The real field is the angular diameter of the sky area which is covered by the apparent field of the eyepiece when used at the optimum observing position. If the apparent field is greater than 45° then the eye will not be able to take it all in at one glance but will need to be moved to look at different parts of the field. It should never be so large as to be greater than the full field of illumination offered by the objective, nor should it be so large as to allow extra-axial aberration to become objectionable.

   If we were to divide the apparent field by the real field we should arrive at the magnification being used:

$$\frac{\text{apparent field}}{\text{real field}} = \text{magnification}$$

So if any two of these values are known, the other may be found. From this it may be gathered that low powers should be employed if a large field of view is required.

Chapter 5

Telescope faults

Chromatic aberration

Chromatic aberration only applies to refractors as reflectors do not suffer from it. It results from the fact that light of shorter wavelength is refracted more than light of longer wavelength. Therefore, the colours making up white light are not brought to the same point of focus. In effect the lens is acting as a prism, the violet and blue rays being focused closer to the objective lens than the red. It is possible to reduce this effect by constructing an objective which combines two or more components of different material. Here the individual chromatic aberration of one component should cancel out that of the other. It can never be completely cured, though triple element lenses do come close to doing so. The effect is to show objects having a red fringeing when inside the focus, those objects assuming a bluish colour when outside focus. It is more noticeable with lenses of short f ratio.

Chromatic aberration also occurs in the eyepiece, see chapter 6.

Spherical aberration

If a mirror has a curvature which is spherical, rays of light reflected toward the optical axis by the outer parts of the mirror arrive at that axis closer to the mirror than do light rays reflected from its central parts. The effect of this would be far greater in mirrors of short f ratio. What we are getting is a number of images strewn out along a section of the optical axis so it would be impossible to achieve a true focus. Even if we could find the position of best focus, the star image would appear as a blob, not a sharp point source. The blob would also be surrounded by a good deal of light which has not been brought to focus.

The problem may not be particularly noticeable with low powers but it will become worse as power is increased. It is far more damaging visually, to the image, than chromatic aberration.

Spherical aberration also occurs in the eyepiece, see Chapter 6.

Coma

This is an extra-axial aberration. With a reflector the amount of the field of view which is free from distortion is limited. Though star images near the centre of the field, resulting from objects close to the optical axis, appear as sharp points of light, those near the edge of the field appear pear shaped, being brighter at the apex. This is actually the point image of the star fading off into the wider section. Though this effect is not obvious with longer focal ratio, it becomes a problem below f6. It is annoying visually and quite damaging for photography. This was a major problem which Schmidt overcame when he developed his very short f ratio, wide field Schmidt camera.

Another way in which coma will become apparent is if the alignment of the optics is not exact. The flaring will be obvious when the optical axis of the mirror is not in line with that of the eyepiece. Proper collimation of the optical train will reduce its effect.

Oblique astigmatism
As with coma, oblique astigmatism arises if an object lies off the optical axis (extra-axial) of the lens or mirror. It therefore mainly affects the outer part of the field. Star images will not focus as points of light but only as a short line, or a rather narrow ellipse. The long axis of the ellipse will appear radial at one position of focus, while tangential at the other.

Distortion
This is an effect where the magnification is not uniform over the whole field of view. It is often explained by using the image of a square which just fits into the field. If the magnification is lower at the centre than at the edge of the field the distortion is of the negative type. This would result in the square having a pincushion shape. If the magnification is lower at the edge of the field than at the centre distortion of the positive type exists and the square will become barrel shaped.

Field curvature
Field curvature is a more serious problem than distortion. It means that as an object moves away from the centre of field refocusing becomes necessary. Usually it is possible to cope with this problem but photographically it is far more serious. To give an idea of what is involved, consider the Schmidt camera. Its field is curved so the photographic plate it uses is itself curved to fit, thus giving sharp images over the whole wide coma-free field.

Chapter 6

Oculars

While it is the job of the objective or mirror to form an image, we need to be able to examine that image and enlarge it by applying varying magnifying powers. This is where the ocular or eyepiece comes in. Usually the ocular consists of two or more lenses. In all cases the lens nearest the objective is called the 'field lens', while that closest to the eye is the 'eye lens'. There are several requirements which should be met and there are many different types of ocular obtainable. Before listing the advantages and disadvantages of the various types, I would like to describe some of the things you might be concerned with.

It is possible to make your own eyepiece but unless you are really handy and a wizard with optics, I would not recommend that you try. Excellent eyepieces can be purchased, although good ones are rather expensive. However, if you do make your own telescope then you can use some of the money saved to purchase a good set of oculars.

There are many cheap and inferior oculars around, using them will ruin the performance of the best telescope, and to try to save money in this way is ill advised. It will be worth your while to check this out. If you know anyone with a set of eyepieces the chances are they will have their favourite and least favourite, ask to try them out with their telescope and you should be left in no doubt about the value of a good eyepiece. I had personal experience of this point only recently. In my observations of comets, use was always made of a good quality orthoscopic eyepiece. Then the acquisition of a new high quality 1 in (26 mm) Plossl underlined the above. It was costly, but contrast, sharpness and detail were so improved that it was like using a new telescope. My advice, then, is that you pay for good eyepieces in the first place. There is no point in buying cheaper ones only to end up buying better later on. This is false economy.

So what should you look for in a good eyepiece? Some, it must be said, are better suited to a particular type of work and to particular types of telescope. Some perform well with telescopes of short focal ratio, while others can only best be used with large focal ratios such as the refractor type. The following lists some of the terms used in describing eyepiece performance.

Eye relief

Some eyepieces have far better eye relief than others. It is the optimum distance at which the eye should be positioned from the face of the eye lens while still able to see all of the field of view. The smaller the eye relief, the closer you have to get your eye to the eye lens, and the less comfortable it will be to view.

Ghost images

When viewing bright stars, or brighter planets, some eyepieces will show faint ghost images. This can be a problem when looking for either close fainter companions of bright stars, faint planetary satellites or faint asteroids which may be close to a bright star. Similarly it may be troublesome when looking for faint comets, especially if the ghost is of the extrafocal type. It is advisable to make a note of any eyepiece which does show ghost images and maybe mark it in some way.

It is possible to check this when viewing, before believing what you see. If the position of the bright object is moved in the field of the telescope, the position of the ghost will change with respect to it. This will not happen if it is a real object.

Magnification

This has already been discussed with regard to the function of the telescope, however, there are certain points that should be covered when considering the eyepiece.

It is quite easy to work out the magnification of a telescope with a given eyepiece, simply divide the focal length of the objective by that of the eyepiece. For example:

	Objective f1	Eyepiece f1		Magnification
in	48	$\frac{1}{2}$	=	96
mm	1219.2	12.7	=	96

This will apply with any instrument regardless of aperture.

The longer the eyepiece focal length, the lower will be the magnification, while the field of view will be large. Longer focal length eyepieces are ideal for deep sky work and for comets. Short focal length eyepieces will give higher magnification but the field will be smaller. These are best suited for lunar and planetary work, where fine detail is required but area of sky not important.

Spherical aberration

Most eyepieces will suffer from this to a larger or lesser extent. It is most obvious with low powers on an instrument of small f ratio. For most purposes it is not a particularly bad fault and has a similar effect to either over or under correction of the objective. It may be detected by examining the image of a star both slightly inside and outside the focus, to see if there is a marked difference. Try different eyepieces to ensure it is an eyepiece problem.

Chromatic aberration

As mentioned in the section on telescope faults reflectors are free of chromatic aberration. If they do show signs of this fault it will almost certainly result either from an atmospheric effect, due to the object under observation being too low in the sky, or it will be a fault in the eyepiece. This can be determined by observing an object which is higher than 30°. The effect should be minimal. To test the eyepiece thoroughly look at the horizontal part of a television aerial against a bright sky with a reflector, employing the eyepiece in question. If it appears fringed with red when inside the focus and blue when outside, then the eyepiece is suffering from this defect.

Curvature of field

A difference in focus between the centre and edge of the field. While irritating visually, photographically it is a real problem.

Chromatic difference of focus

Bright objects will show strong prismatic colours, as they are moved away from the centre of field.

Chapter 7

Eyepiece types

Now we have considered the common faults we may find in the eyepiece, let us look at the more popular types in turn and see what advantages and disadvantages they have. We are looking for perfection but we will never find it. Ideally we would like an eyepiece that has a wide, dark flat field, free from ghosts. It should have good definition with freedom from aberrations, good eye relief and a bright image, with minimum loss of light through internal reflection of lens surfaces. Most modern eyepieces now have all surfaces bloomed to counter the latter, improving transmission.

The Huyghenian

The construction of this eyepiece uses two plano convex lenses with flat sides facing the eye and an internal field stop between the lenses. It has a good large angular field, free from distortion except near the edge. The field though is rather curved. Eye relief is reasonable. It has rather bad spherical aberration and is best used on longer f ratio telescopes, being suitable for refractors of around f15-f20. Chromatic aberration becomes noticeable at short f ratios.

They are ideal for high power use of 25D or greater. There are no ghosts with this eyepiece which is often used with microscopes. Transmission is slightly over 80 per cent, 90 per cent if coated.

Figure 18. The Huyghenian eyepiece.

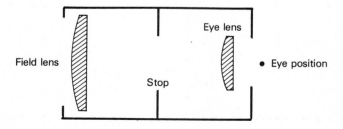

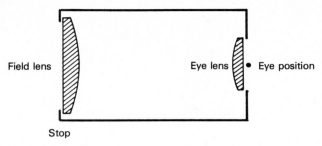

Figure 19. The Ramsden eyepiece.

Ramsden

This has two plano convex lenses with convex sides facing each other. It has a 40-50° field of view though this is only useful out to about 35°. The field is flatter and spherical aberration less than with the Huyghenian, but eye relief is very small indeed, making it a rather uncomfortable eyepiece to use. It has considerable chromatic difference of magnification and suffers with ghosts which are out of focus. Because of its flatter field, it can be used with lower f ratio instruments and is particularly useful as a finder eyepiece.

Transmission is slightly over 80 per cent, 90 per cent when coated which is identical to the Huyghenian. The Ramsden suffers from slight distortion and astigmatism outside the useful 35° field.

Kellner and Achromatic Ramsden

The Achromatic Ramsden can generally be regarded as a modern version of the Kellner which is why they are described together. Each has a plano convex field lens with an achromatic cemented doublet eye lens. Ideal for low power work, giving a good wide flat field of around 45-60° apparent diameter. There is a small amount of chromatic aberration, though this is cut down to a minimum by use of the doublet and there is slight curvature of the field at the edge. The crown biconvex element of the eye lens is on the side

Figure 20. The Kellner (a) and Achromatic Ramsden (b) eyepieces.

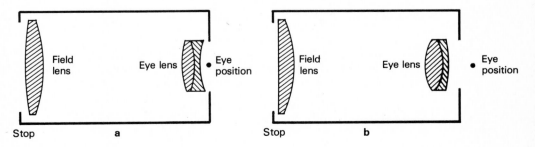

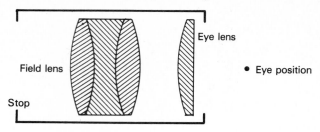

Figure 21. The Orthoscopic eyepiece.

nearest the field lens, while the flint element is closest to the eye. Flint is a softer glass than crown, so having a surface of flint unprotected leaves it open to damage by scratching so great care must be taken when cleaning it.

Eye relief is not as good with the Kellner as it is with the Achromatic Ramsden and the former is more plagued by ghosts. This problem has been much improved by coating the lenses in more modern makes of this eyepiece. Generally it is highly regarded and often used in binoculars.

Transmission for both types of eyepiece is slightly under 80 per cent, 89 per cent when coated.

Orthoscopic

The Orthoscopic is regarded as the best all-round eyepiece. It has a plano convex eye lens and a cemented triple achromat field lens. It has a dark wide flat field ranging from 35-50° with excellent correction of spherical and chromatic aberration. It is free from ghosts and has excellent eye relief. It is useful with telescopes of low focal ratio such as f5 or lower. The outer components are of crown glass and so resistant to scratching. There are variants of this eyepiece, Figure 21 showing the most common.

The main disadvantage of Orthoscopic eyepieces is their high cost but

Figure 22. The Tolles eyepiece.

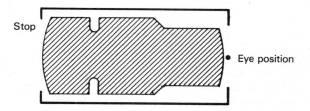

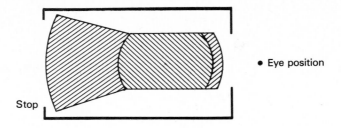

Figure 23. The Monocentric eyepiece.

they truly are worth having, and are favourites with most astronomers. Transmission is 83 per cent, 90 per cent when coated.

Tolles
A Tolles eyepiece could be called a solid Huyghenian. It is a rod of solid crown glass which has spherical ends. There is only a small amount of spherical and chromatic aberration. The field is dark and free from ghosts. Eye relief is very poor and the eyepiece is best suited to medium f ratios of around f6-f8. It has excellent definition at the centre of field and transmission is good, due to lack of internal lens surfaces, at 85 per cent it is better in fact than the Huyghenian.

The field is only 30° and owing to the very poor eye relief not all of it can be seen. It is a good eyepiece for planetary work where field size is not so important.

Monocentric
This eyepiece is a cemented triplet, the components of which have surfaces which are parts of concentric spheres. It is regarded by many as probably the most perfect eyepiece. It is particularly suited to Newtonian reflectors of short f ratio, but not above f6. It suffers from slight spherical aberration. The field is dark and flat though smallish at around 25°. It is free from ghosts and has reasonable eye relief, though there is some light loss due to absorption through the thickness of the glass. Transmission however is still excellent at 88 per cent and when coated is as high as 92 per cent.

Wide field five- and six-element types
There are many variations of these wide field eyepieces which have very wide fields of 70° and even as high as 80-90°. The Erfle is perhaps the best known. They do, however, tend to suffer from distortion near the outer edge of the field. With having so many elements, light loss can be considerable. They are best used for comet hunting and comets displaying long tails, though the poor transmission can be a disadvantage here.

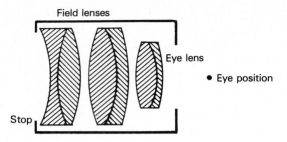

Figure 24. The wide field six-element-type eyepiece.

Until recently all types were only found as government surplus. Lately they have been manufactured specially but tend to be rather more expensive than the government surplus ones. Another problem is that the outer element of the eye lens is made of softer flint glass and is susceptible to scratching. Actual transmission is 70 per cent, 84 per cent if coated.

The above seems to paint a poor picture but despite all the faults it is a pleasure to use these eyepieces. The wide field is most impressive and it is well worth putting up with the other problems. Views of the Moon, large star fields and bigger comets are really spectacular.

Plossl or Dialsight

A Plossl or Dialsight eyepiece consists of two achromatic doublets which may be symmetrical, or nearly so. It has a large flat field which can be 40-50°, the eye relief is excellent but can be less with the larger field. The flint elements of each doublet are on the outside, so, again, care has to be taken not to scratch them. Transmission is good at just under 80 per cent and nearly 88 per cent when coated. An excellent eyepiece in recently manufactured forms.

Figure 25. The Plossl or Dialsight eyepiece.

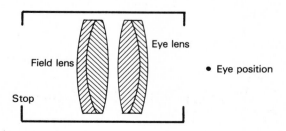

Working out magnification

Many readers will wish to know the exact magnification they are getting from a particular eyepiece and I have shown how this is worked out provided one knows its focal length. Most modern eyepieces have their focal length engraved on the barrel and this makes things easy. However, older eyepieces will not be so marked, especially war or government surplus ones. If you have acquired such an eyepiece second-hand, and wish to find out its focal length or even wish to check that those marked are done so correctly, with only a little trouble this may be done in the following way.

The pencil of rays emerging from the eyepiece is the exit pupil and a cross-section of this is known as the Ramsden disc. Point the telescope up toward a bright daylight sky and the Ramsden disc should be visible 'ghost like' just behind the eyepiece. Place a piece of ground glass screen behind the eyepiece and measure this disc at the point where the focus is sharpest. Now if you divide the objective diameter by the diameter of the exit pupil this will give the magnification. It therefore becomes easy to work out the eyepiece focal length, because the magnification is the sum of the objective's focal length divided by the eyepiece's focal length.

So: Objective diameter 6 in (152 mm)
Objective focal length f8 or 48 in (1219.2 mm)
Diameter of exit pupil ⅛ in (3 mm)

$$\frac{6 \text{ in}}{⅛ \text{ in}} = 48 \text{ so} \frac{48 \text{ in}}{48} = 1 \text{ in}$$

Therefore the focal length of the eyepiece is 1 in (25.4 mm).

The Barlow lens

There are many who do not advocate use of a Barlow lens, so let us look at what it does, considering the advantages and disadvantages.

By using a Barlow lens the effective focal length of the objective can be increased, and, by its combination with a long focus eyepiece, the magnify-

Figure 26. The Barlow lens.

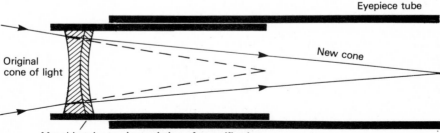

Eyepiece tube

Original cone of light

New cone

Movable tube to give variation of magnification

ing power of that eyepiece can be increased. This cuts down the need for more eyepieces of varying types. We can also make use of the large eye relief afforded by some long focal length eyepieces, even when now obtaining a higher power.

The Barlow itself is a negative lens which can either be a cemented or separate crown and flint doublet, or even a simple single-element lens. When placed in the converging cone of light from the objective it changes the angle of convergence, making it longer, as though it were from an objective of greater f ratio. It is mounted in its own tube and this is made to slide into a wider tube which takes the desired eyepiece at one end. By moving this tube in and out we can vary the magnification of the Barlow/eyepiece combination.

Though it may introduce extra errors into the system, if well made the Barlow will almost certainly remove more errors than it creates. Poorer type eyepieces, such as the Huyghenian, will benefit from its use when short f ratio Newtonians are used. It also cuts out the need for eyepieces that would have a ridiculously short focal length.

There is a limit to the use of a Barlow. The maximum range of positions is from the prime focus of the objective to a point inward equal to the focal length of the Barlow itself. The ratio of the two cone angles gives the magnification. The formula for working out the magnification is given in *The Amateur Astronomer's Handbook* (see Bibliography).

*   *   *

So, what eyepieces might be chosen as a good all-round selection for your observatory?

If cost is a consideration, and this must be kept as low as possible, then I suggest a minimum of three eyepieces: a low power to give around 5D-6D, which will be useful for deep sky work, comet seeking and the observation of large scale cometary phenomena; a second to give medium magnification of around 15D, for smaller scale cometary features, more detailed deep sky work, such as globular clusters, planetary nebulae and variable stars, also planetary and lunar detail on poor nights; lastly a high power eyepiece giving around 25D-30D, for planetary and lunar work plus double star work on fine nights. This selection would benefit from the addition of a good Barlow lens.

When purchasing these eyepieces, try to buy as good a make as you can possibly afford. If they are all of the same type it may be possible to obtain a set that are parfocal, meaning that each eyepiece is made so that it is brought to focus at the same position as the others of the set. This is a great advantage when observing objects like Venus and Mercury during the daytime. These objects can easily be lost when changing eyepieces because of the need to refocus with non-parfocal types.

When choosing the eyepieces it is advisable to go for those which have a

Figure 27. An eyepiece box can be made to take other accessories such as eyepiece draw tubes, Barlow lens, adaptors etc. It is a way to keep everything together, making things easily accessible in the dark.

1¼ in (32 mm) outside diameter rather than the cheaper eyepieces with a 1 in (25.4 mm) outside diameter barrel. Though the latter can be quite good they are never so good as those with larger outside diameter barrels.

When you have acquired your eyepieces, great care should be taken at all times to ensure they are kept in perfect condition. They should never be put into your pocket or left lying around a dark observatory just asking to be knocked on to the floor. Ideally a wooden box should be made to hold them. The box should be deeper than the largest of the eyepieces in length and it should have a false bottom or shelf into which a number of holes have been cut. The holes should have diameters slightly larger than the outside diameter of the parts of the eyepieces that fit into the drawtube of the telescope. These will either be 1 in (25.4 mm) 1¼ in (32 mm) or 2 in (50 mm). When placed into position the eyepieces should still be clear of the box bottom. Pad the lid with sponge or chamois leather with cotton wool backing. The idea of this is to hold the eyepieces softly in position when the lid is shut and not allow them to rattle about. If you wish you could make the box to accept other accessories so that in the dark you will know where everything is. Put a small hook on to hold the lid shut and a handle fastened to the box base, not to the lid as if this comes open your precious eyepieces will spill on to the floor. Now paint the box white so that it can be seen in the dark. The whole lot can then be taken out at night and brought back into the house after use, where they will benefit from being kept warm and dry.

Chapter 8

Telescope mountings

To use a telescope properly and to see all that it is capable of showing, it must be held firmly in some way while remaining movable, so that it can be directed to any part of the sky easily. Once any amount of magnification is employed to view an object, movement and vibration are also magnified. With high powers the slightest vibration seems enormous. No doubt you will have suffered this problem when using only a pair of binoculars. Unless you can rest them on something, the object you wish to see moves around making it difficult to examine. If you have used both 7 × 50 and 10 × 50 types, those magnifying 10× will show this effect far more than those magnifying 7×. Imagine then the problems encountered when using powers of 300×. It becomes absolutely essential to have a mount that is very steady indeed. Even a slight breeze can make life very difficult.

Telescope mounts can be either portable, if the telescope is small to moderate in size, or permanent for the larger instrument. There is no rule that states just where one draws the line between the portable and permanent. There are some who mount their 6 in (152 mm) telescopes permanently while others have designed mounts for up to 30 in (76 cm) instruments which are still portable and can be moved, on trailers, to different observing locations which are better than their home sites. This practice is quite common in America where astronomers living among the bright lights of major cities would not be able to carry out observing programmes in any other way.

Generally the permanent mount will be the firmer but it is a good idea when setting up your observatory to try to do both. Often, even though you have a good observing site in your own garden, there will be some obstruction, your house for instance, that will hide a large part of the sky. You can bet that if you make a permanent pier telescope, some object of exceptional interest will appear in that part of the sky inaccessible to you. If, therefore, you have a smaller portable telescope at least you can do something about it. My own observatory has a permanently mounted 16½ in (419 mm) reflector but I have also portable 10 in (254 mm), 4 in (102 mm) and 3 in (76 mm) telescopes. I have been glad to have these on occasions when bright comets have not been in view to the larger instrument. It has also given me the opportunity to take one or other of the smaller telescopes out into the country, away from any artificial lights. In this way I have taken photographs which are far better than they would have been from my home site because of street lighting.

In mounting a telescope there are many requirements which have to be met and there are a number of basic designs which have been developed to meet these. As in previous chapters, there now follows a list describing the more common types of mounting arrangements so that you may make your own choice. First though let us have a look at the various requirements.

Any mounting, if it is to work properly, must allow two rotations of movement around axes which are at right angles to each other. If one axis of rotation is perpendicular then rotational movement will follow a path parallel to the horizon, while the other will always trace a path which is vertical to the horizon, irrespective of which direction it is pointing. This type of mount is called an altazimuth, since it permits movement in *alt*itude (swinging round a horizontal axis) and *azimuth* (swinging round a vertical axis).

If we were to tilt the vertical axis until it were parallel to the rotational axis of the Earth it would obviously have a different degree of tilt depending on your latitude. This vertical axis would remain vertical if you were at the Earth's poles but it would tilt more and more as you moved toward the equator. At the equator itself that axis would become horizontal. Because of this alignment with the Earth's poles the axis is referred to as the polar axis. The result now will be that wherever your position on Earth, the rotation in azimuth will follow a path parallel to the Earth's equator. This happens to be the way astronomical objects move due to diurnal motion, or the apparent motion of the celestial sphere due to the axial rotation of the Earth—the motion which brings about the daily rising and setting of the Sun and stars.

What we have therefore, is a mount which naturally follows the movement of the stars and is called an equatorial. It is much more convenient than the altazimuth though not so easy to construct. Generally the altazimuth is quite adequate for casual use.

To reconcile the movements of an equatorial mount with co-ordinates in the sky, the left to right motion is referred to as movement in right ascension (RA) and movements perpendicular to this as motion in declination (Dec). If we can now add some form of motor drive to the polar axis which achieves one full east-west rotation each 24 hours, we now have a synchronous movement, which effectively cancels out the rotation of the Earth. In this way, providing the settings and drive are accurate, we will be able to keep objects of interest centred in the field of view, whenever they are above the horizon. If there is no motor drive then objects would just drift through the field making continual adjustments necessary. Even without the drive it is far easier to do this with an equatorial, since adjustment need only be made in one axis. With the altazimuth, adjustments are continually required on both axes and a motor drive, in normal circumstances, is not practical.

Further, perhaps less important though highly desirable, requirements

Figure 28. The 12½ in (32 cm) refractor of Keele University Observatory on its German equatorial mount. This sort of mount is ideally suited to the refractor, for which it was originally designed. It is, however, also a very popular mount for reflectors. (Keele University.)

are that the mount be compact which usually adds to its stability. It should be simple to construct and relatively inexpensive. It should give access to all parts of the sky—some mounts do not allow access to the pole. Finally the observing positions afforded by the mount should be comfortable and easy to reach. Given the basic requirements let us now look at the various designs.

The German equatorial

This is probably still the most common form of equatorial mounting. It was designed by Fraunhöfer whose best example is the great Dorpat refractor. Though most suited to smaller instruments it was used for the great refractors built during the last half of the nineteenth century, including the 26 in (66 cm) Washington, 36 in (91 cm) Lick and 40 in (101 cm) Yerkes refractors.

Basically, the telescope is held in a cradle of sufficient size to support the tube. This is attached to one end of the declination axis and counterbalanced by a large weight fixed to the other end. This declination axis is joined at its centre of balance by the polar axis, forming a T. Bearings at both the polar and declination axes allow smooth movement. Some form of clutch arrangement is necessary to retard this movement, which would otherwise be too free. The main right ascension drive is applied to the polar axis shaft. It should be possible to adjust the angle of the polar axis to facilitate its alignment at different latitudes. This, plus an adjustment of the head for azimuth, will allow accurate setting of the head for guiding purposes.

All of the sky cannot be covered when the telescope is positioned at one or the other side of the head. When guiding for long periods it will eventually come into contact with the pier, thus arresting its movement. By use of both sides the whole sky does become accessible, but even then some positions near the zenith (point overhead) are less convenient when the mount is used with a refractor than when used with a relfector. To move the telescope from one side to the other simply requires half of one full revolution in right ascension and declination. This reversing means that the telescope is inverted and, though a small problem when using it visually, is no good for photography as any exposure being made must be stopped. It always pays to check that there is enough clearance between the tube and the pier before commencing an exposure.

The mount is useful for both refractors and reflectors though a much higher pier will be required for the former and for Cassegrain type reflectors. The pier for the equatorial head can be a single concrete or steel pillar. For small instruments it can easily be made portable by fixture to a tripod. It is also relatively compact. The major disadvantage, not counting the need for changing the telescope from one side of the mount to the other in prolonged guided sessions, is the fact that, by design, the telescope and counterweight do need to overhang either side of the polar axis to some considerable degree. This tends toward instability.

The fork mounting

This is a very convenient mount offering a great deal for telescopes, even at the large end of the scale. The basic design has a large fork fixed to the top end of a polar axis. All of the sky is accessible and the telescope does not need reversal like the German mount, meaning uninterrupted tracking for prolonged periods, in fact from rising to setting if wished.

There is one similarity between it and the German, this is the way the polar axis is held in its bearings. Declination movement is by bearings at the top of the forks. In order to prevent bending or flexure the mount must be made quite massive, but the design does at least lend itself to this. There is

Figure 29. The fork mount design, used here for the 30 in (76 cm) Thompson reflector of the Royal Greenwich Observatory, Herstmonceaux. It is a popular design used on many modern telescopes. (Royal Greenwich Observatory.)

no need for overhanging counterweights as with the German which helps with rigidity. The only counterweights needed are on the polar axis and possibly around the bottom of the tube to enable the construction of short fork arms. Weight added to the polar axis keeps the centre of gravity very low, once more aiding with rigidity. It is popular with amateurs because it is fairly easy to make. Most of the base and fork can be made with reinforced concrete. A further aid to the stability is to add a large steel disc to the polar axis, which can then run between rollers. This makes for a very solid mount indeed, especially if the polar axis is made into a heavy cone. (See Figure 87.)

The main problem with the mount is that it is not suited to refractors or

Figure 30. The English mount design of the 100 in (250 cm) Hooker telescope at Mount Wilson. Here the instrument is seen pointing south. Note that the mount itself would obstruct the view of the northern polar sky. It is, however, a very popular mount because of its rigidity. (Hale Observatories.)

Cassegrains. Because of the eyepiece position, parts of the sky around the pole can be inaccessible, though an eyepiece diagonal would help here. The same design when scaled down is useful as a mount for very small telescopes and even cameras on their own. Among large telescopes mounted in this way are the Lick 120 in (300 cm), the Mount Wilson 60 in (150 cm) and the Mount Palomar 48 in (122 cm) Schmidt camera.

Drives can be attached to the Polar axis or, if of the type using rollers, it can be attached to an extended shaft through either of these.

The English mounting

Another name for this is the yoke mounting and it might be regarded as a closed fork. There are four bearings used for the movement; one at each of the support points either side of the yoke, which itself becomes the polar axis. The other two are at either side of the declination axis and are supported by the yoke. There are no counterweights needed except possibly on the tube.

It is an extremely rigid structure, again suitable for large telescopes, though there are a few disadvantages. Greatest of these is the fact that it is impossible to view a large area of sky around the pole. Also, unless the tube is in some way rotatable in the yoke, the eyepiece can attain difficult positions. There is also the possibility of flexure with the yoke arms unless these are rigidly made.

Generally the mount is rather large and not easily made portable, however, it is very easy to construct and the piers can be made of reinforced concrete, making it a rather cheap mount. Perhaps the best examples of large telescopes using this form of mount are the 100 in (250 cm) Hooker telescope at Mount Wilson, USA and the 145 in (280 cm) UK Infra-red telescope at Hawaii.

Cross axis mounting

Also known as the modified English mounting, instead of using a yoke this system uses a single beam, with the declination axis bearing placed at its centre. There is need with this design to counter the weight of the telescope on the opposite side of the beam. This can be turned into an advantage because a second telescope can be added here so that it can carry one visual and one photographic telescope. It has the advantage of the rigidity offered by the two points of support to the polar axis, as with the yoke, but the offset telescope now allows accessibility to the sky around the pole. The mount can be used with either a reflector or refractor, being just as good for both.

The cross axis mounting is popular with amateurs, again because of the relative ease of construction. Lorry back axles have been adapted quite successfully for the polar axis beam. It is better made as a permanent mount but can be made portable if fixed to a trailer. Major telescopes using this idea are the 72 in (183 cm) at Dominian Astrophysical Observatory in Canada and the 74 in (190 cm) at Mount Stromlo Observatory in Australia.

Left *Figure 31. The cross axis or modified English mount which, unlike the true English design, does allow access to the polar sky. The instrument shown here is the Yapp 36 in (91 cm) reflector at Herstmonceux. (Royal Greenwich Observatory.)*

Below *Figure 32. Six views of the 200 in (500 cm) Hale reflector in various positions using its east-west and north-south motions. The mount of this instrument is basically a yoke or English mount but the north bearing is in the form of a giant horseshoe allowing access to the polar sky with the greater rigidity of the English mount. The idea originally grew out of a design by Russell W. Porter known as the split ring, but the horseshoe mount itself has been credited largely to three men; namely J.A. Anderson, R.E. Edgar and M. Serrurier. Modified versions of this are now used for many giant reflectors. (Hale Observatories.)*

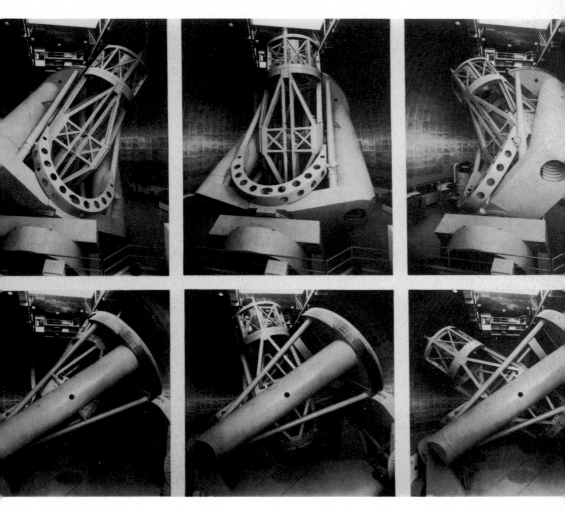

Horseshoe mounting

This was basically a yoke mounting design. The uppermost polar axis bearing ring is huge and has a U shaped cut-out to allow the telescope access to the polar sky. It was originally designed for the Mount Palomar 200 in (500 cm) reflector, but modified versions of it are used with the 158 in (400 cm) Kitt Peak, 158 in (400 cm) Cerro Tololo, Chile and the 153 in (380 cm) Anglo Australian telescope at Siding Spring. With these three, unlike the Mount Palomar telescope, the declination axis is supported within the horseshoe bearing itself.

Altazimuth mounting

This is the most simple and cheap to make. It is easy to use for casual looking at the sky but long exposure photographs are not possible with it because its motion does not match those of the heavenly bodies. The one area where it can be useful is for comet seeking. When carrying out this sort of work it is best to section off the sky for the search pattern and the altazimuth is ideal for this. The method saves going over the same area of sky more than once. It is possible to do this with an equatorial but it is not so easy to keep check on the limits of sweep areas.

In these days, when computers are becoming so sophisticated, major telescopes are now using altazimuth mounts. These allow the complex tracking movements required with such mounts to be carried out. The advantage in being able to use them with large telescopes is their lower cost. They do not need to be as massive as equatorials built to take similar size instruments. The largest example of this type of mounting, perhaps surprisingly, is that of the world's largest telescope, the 236 in (600 cm) reflector in the Soviet Union.

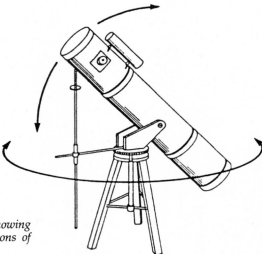

Figure 33. The altazimuth mount showing the general design and two directions of movement.

Part Two

Chapter 9

Building your own telescope

Because of the belief that to build a telescope is exceedingly difficult, and to do so requires great skill, many people instantly dismiss the idea. Yet it is possible to build very good telescopes without great skill. Anyone who has a certain amount of ordinary ability can produce an instrument that will have astounding quality. In most cases it will be far better than telescopes made by some professional manufacturers. The feeling of satisfaction in constructing your own instrument will be great. What could be better than viewing the celestial objects in glorious detail through an instrument that you yourself are entirely responsible for.

There are many facets to the art of telescope building. Few would-be telescope builders have the same ideas, or go about things in the same way. There are two or three groups that constructors can be loosely slotted into. First, there are those who build telescopes just because it is an engineering achievement. Secondly there are those who are basically opticians, gaining their satisfaction from creating a lens of supreme accuracy. Finally there are those who simply build the telescope as a means to an end. They are only interested in what the instrument will show them once completed. It must be said though, that many do not end up in the category they started out in. It can happen that one, initially interested in observing, can be so taken up in telescope construction that eventually it is in this he finds his vocation.

Personally I fall into the third category—observational work is my main aim, but even so I find now that building an instrument gives as much pleasure as looking through it. I have been lucky however, by retaining a major interest in observation I have been able to find great satisfaction from the construction and use of the more simple design of telescope, not becoming bogged down in over sophistication. If therefore you have the same interest, which is, after all, why telescopes were developed in the first place, simply made instruments can achieve as much as you could ever hope for. A little imagination, some spare time and perhaps slightly more than average patience and perseverance are all that will be required. Believe me, the pleasure gained far outweighs the work put in, so let's look at just what does need to be done.

Personally I am no expert mirror maker and for this reason I sympathize with those who will prefer to purchase ready-made mirrors. These can be obtained sometimes quite easily at reasonable cost. Doing things this way will save time for those not particularly interested in the art of mirror making. However, to make the mirror will make the telescope truly your own and will obviously save money. The construction of your mirror, or acquisition of it, is of paramount importance. You can design your instrument first but you would be unwise to build it before you have the optics. It is far easier to adjust the design of the telescope than to alter the figure of a mirror to suit. This should become apparent later.

Your choice of optics and telescope design will need to be based on the sort of work you wish to do. The notes on the various designs of telescope should help you reach a decision. You will probably find that there are three major considerations; situation, requirements and cost. Not everyone is fortunate enough to live in the country with masses of spare land to give up to an observatory. As it is also unusual for the average astronomer to specialize in the first instance, you are likely to require a telescope which is adaptable and varied in its applications. Finally the important question of cost is bound to be a consideration, particularly so for anyone just starting, not really knowing just how interested they are likely to become.

In this second section of the book it is my intention to take you stage by stage through the construction of a telescope which can meet all of these requirements. I have already described the Newtonian reflector and I feel that it is bound to be a popular choice for the novice and even the seasoned astronomer. This type of instrument can be large or small and so simple as to keep cost to a minimum. Let us, then, go through the construction of such a telescope, from the making of the optics to the building of a housing to protect both instrument and observer.

Chapter 10

Construction of the mirror

As we have already established, the most important components of any telescope are the optics. They are also the most costly and difficult to make. If you decide to save time and energy by purchasing your mirror, then I advise you do this via a reputable dealer. You should ask for details of the mirror's quality in writing. If the dealer will not give this, find one who will. On receipt of the mirror it is a good idea to have it independently tested, or even test it yourself by a method to be discussed later in this section. I have found through bitter experience that mirrors made, even by so called reputable dealers, are not always as good as they are made out to be. Some I am afraid tend to live on their past reputation. If you find it inferior, return it and request it be improved to the standard for which you are paying.

Provided you have the time and patience there is a lot to be said for making your own mirror. What follows is a guide to the process.

The first thing you have to do when intending to make a mirror is to decide on the aperture of the telescope you are going to build. Useful sizes range from 6-12 in (152-304 mm). The larger the mirror you choose, the greater will be the difficulties encountered in its making and in the subsequent construction of the telescope in which it must be placed. For this reason I advise choosing a mirror of 6 in (152 mm).

You need to obtain a glass disc or blank, as it is called. These can be obtained from optical firms or telescope manufacturers without any difficulty. There are one or two things you should look for depending on which material the blank is made of.

If the blank is of low expansion type glass it will be more expensive than one of ordinary plate glass. In the past Pyrex has been regarded as a good material but there are always many bubbles in it. As you start to grind the blank, in the process of mirror making, these bubbles, if close to the surface, will become small holes in the mirror face. So, if your blank is Pyrex, check to see which surface is most likely to be free from such bubbles and grind that surface. If it is found that large bubbles are close to the surface then the blank is no use and should be returned. If it appears that there are no large bubbles closer than ⅛ in (3 mm) to the surface, then there should be no problem. Another low expansion material called Duran 50 is very popular. It is quite expensive compared with plate glass, presently 50 per cent more. Many people prefer these low expansion materials because of their resistance to temperature changes. Plate glass will be quite adequate for a mirror of 6 in (152 mm), however.

Apart from the mirror disc a second blank will be required. This will act as the tool when making the mirror. It need not be of low expansion glass, even if the mirror itself is. It also need not be so thick. For a mirror of the size we are dealing with, we need a blank around 1 in (25 mm) thick, while the tool thickness need only be around ⅝ in (15 mm).

If the blank is of plate glass then the flattest and smoothest surface should be used. Before actually starting on the rough grinding the front edges of the mirror and tool must be bevelled using a medium grade carborundum stone. When doing this it is very easy to chip the glass, so great care must be taken. The mirror, or tool, and the stone must be kept wet and the working angle of the stone should be 45°. Strokes must always be away from the mirror. If you bring the stone back over the mirror the glass will certainly chip.

The bevel is very important and should be around ⅛ in (3 mm) wide. It is possible to manage with a narrower bevel but it is ill advised. The mirror edge will become very sharp during the grinding process and small chips could well end up between the mirror and tool, things just happen that way. Deep scratches in the mirror's surface will result and I do not have to tell you what the effect would be if this should happen toward the end of the fine grinding stage. The whole process of rough grinding would need to be re-started and there is nothing to say it would not happen again and again. It will become apparent throughout this section just what extra work would be caused; by having a decent bevel to start with, all that could be saved.

Once the bevel is thought satisfactory, the time has come to begin work on making your mirror. To do this the surface of the glass has to be hollowed out to a certain depth, giving a certain radius of curvature. Just what this curvature needs to be depends on what focal ratio you require for your mirror. If you are to make a 6 in mirror, which is to be used for observations of the Moon and planets, then an ideal focal ratio is eight times the mirror diameter (f8) or 48 in (120 cm). If a rich field telescope is required for comet or deep sky work, then f4 would be better. This would be a focal length of 24 in (61 cm). For the latter a much deeper curve would be required, which means more glass needs to be removed and therefore more work in the grinding stage is necessary. For your first attempt f8 is the better choice.

So for a 6 in mirror of 48 in focal length, the mirror has to be hollowed out to a specific depth. It so happens that the radius of the curve of a mirror's surface needs to be twice the focal length required for the mirror. Therefore, in our case, the radius of curvature must be 96 in (243 cm).

How will you know when the correct depth of curve has been reached? There are two ways to do this. The first is simply to place a straight edge across a central axis of the mirror and measure the gap by passing an object

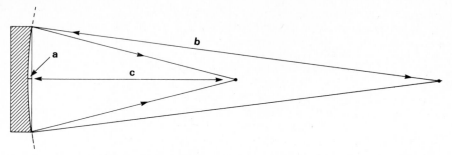

Figure 34. Diagram to show (a) sagitta, (b) radius of curvature and (c) focal length.

of known thickness through it. The thickness of the object should be equal to that which you require for the depth of curve and when it just passes through the gap you will know you have achieved the correct depth of curve or sagitta. Another, possibly easier, method is to cut a template out of stiff card or thin aluminium sheet which has the correct radius of curvature. When this fits the hollow of the mirror then enough glass has been removed.

The formula for working out the correct sagitta is quite simple and is as follows:

$$\text{Sagitta} = \frac{r^2}{2R}$$

r = radius of mirror
R = radius of curvature of mirror's spherical surface.

For a 6 in (152 mm) the radius is 3 in (76 mm) and for f8 the radius of curvature is 96 in (243 cm).

Therefore:

$$\frac{3^2}{2 \times 96} = \frac{9}{192} = .0468 \text{ in}$$

You therefore need a depth of slightly over $1/20$ in (1.18 mm).

To hollow out the glass is, in theory, an easy though time-consuming task. Put simply it is done by placing the two pieces of glass together with abrasive and water between them. By moving them in a certain way, to be described, the uppermost piece of glass (the mirror) becomes concave while the lower piece (the tool) becomes convex. By following a laid-down, tried and tested process anyone can produce a mirror of supreme quality. What follows are basic instructions based on my own experience, cutting out fussiness. It is however, detailed enough to enable success. Each individual will find short cuts and variations to suit their own temperament. This will be to the good. What should be avoided is rigid adherence to a set pattern which will introduce errors. Do not be afraid to vary things a little.

The actual movements required to obtain the correct shape are simply to push the mirror back and forth over the tool using fairly long strokes and changing direction every so often. During the process the mirror will be ground more in the centre than at the edges, simply because the glass is continually in contact there while the edges lose contact with each stroke. Let us look at each stage of the mirror-making procedure in some detail.

Rough grinding

When a decent bevel has been achieved and a template made to gauge depth of curve, the tool should now be fixed to a flat surface such as an old table. This should be a round table if possible as it will be far easier to move around it during the grinding process. The tool is fixed by three cleats placed at 120° intervals around its edge. Just trace a circle around the tool and align the cleats with this. Obviously the part of the cleat which is to be in contact with the edge of the tool must not be allowed to protrude above its surface, but should be a small distance below it. Make the cleats wedge shaped so that they slope away from the mirror. Countersink and screw them to the table surface at such an angle that they tend to hold the mirror gently in place, as shown in Figure 35.

The following abrasives will be needed; Carborundum 80, 120, 220, 280 and Aloxite 400, 600 and 1,000 and cerium oxide. The abrasives should be handled with great care to ensure that they do not become contaminated with foreign material such as dust, or coarser grade particles of abrasive. If they do become contaminated, scratching of the mirror surface will result.

Figure 35. Method of securing tool or mirror to the table for grinding and polishing. The three cleats used should be spaced at 120° intervals, be wedge shaped and not allowed to protrude above the mirror surface.

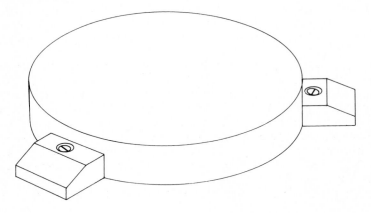

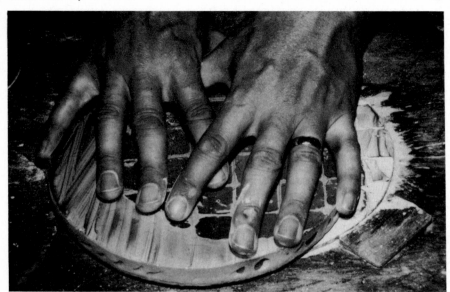

Figure 36. The hand position for grinding and polishing. Do not allow the fingers to hang too far over the edge. (This photograph shows the mirror on the lap during the polishing process.)

When the tool has been placed between the cleats, preferably with two or three pieces of wet paper underneath it, spray the surface with water using a plant spray which can be adjusted to give a fine mist. Sprinkle a little 80 grade abrasive on to the wet surface then spray with water again, not so much as to swill the abrasive away but sufficient to allow it to remain loose during grinding, and not sticky. Slightly too much water is better than too little. This will be felt as the grinding process is commenced. You will be able to judge the effect of the abrasive quite easily. With more water it will sound and feel rougher and this will permit faster grinding. If the abrasive becomes sticky it will not be so effective, grinding much more slowly, though much harder to move.

You must hold the mirror in a certain way. Do not allow the finger tips to hang over the edge of the mirror too far, otherwise heat from them will transfer to the mirror surface, expanding the glass slightly in certain parts, this could affect the final figure. The problem will of course be greater with plate glass than with low expansion materials. When glass heats up in a small area a hill is formed. This will be ground out and when the mirror cools it will become a hollow. Obviously it will only be slight but we are talking of achieving a very accurate optical surface and a few millionths of an inch can matter a great deal.

Push the mirror back and forth over the tool with a stroke of such length that allows the centre of the mirror to approach to within 1 in (25 mm) of each side of the tool, which will give an overall stroke length of not more than 4 in (102 mm) for a 6 in (152 mm) mirror. You should aim at a speed of roughly one second for each back and forward movement.

At the end of each half dozen strokes take one step to the left or right, whichever you prefer, but once you have decided on your direction, stick to it. With each step turn the mirror in the opposite direction slightly, ie if you are moving around the table in a clockwise direction rotate the mirror anti-clockwise. Do this for one complete circuit of the table and continue in this manner until you feel the abrasive action start to weaken. This means the abrasive is starting to break down and it is largely a matter of judgement. Renew the abrasive and water and continue with the process.

After this need for renewal of abrasive and water has occurred about six times, wash the mirror and tool for checking. On doing so you will note that the mirror has been ground slightly in the centre while the tool is showing signs of grinding around its edge. Continue this process a further com-parable amount of time—six abrasive recharges—and check again to monitor progress. At this point the template described earlier can be used to check the curve of the hollowed out section of the mirror.

When a section of the mirror approximately one third of the total diameter has been hollowed out and the template is seen in part to fit this hollow, the time will have come to shorten the strokes. At the end of each new stroke only one third of the mirror should overhang the tool. This will have the effect of widening the area of mirror that is ground, but it will not deepen the hollow. With the gradual increase in diameter of the ground area continue to shorten the strokes. By doing this, when the whole surface of the mirror has been ground, a check with the template should hopefully show it to fit the curve quite closely, if you are lucky. More than likely on your first attempt it will not. Not to worry though, things can be put right fairly easily.

If you can see a slight gap under the template at the centre of the mirror, continue grinding with a stroke of a length to give a one third overhang of the mirror on the tool. This will very quickly correct the problem so do not go on too long, checking quite often with the template. If all of the curve is deeper than the template, meaning you have a shorter radius of curvature than required, place the mirror between the cleats instead of the tool, then proceed to grind with the tool itself. In this case a shorter type stroke must be used which will have the effect of taking out the curve. Checking must again be done regularly since it will soon be corrected.

With luck your first attempt should find the rough grinding completed in about four to five hours. Occasionally it may take longer but with practice it can be considerably reduced. When satisfied that the curve is correct wash off the abrasive from the mirror, tool and the whole table top. Make sure no old abrasive remains lurking in the nooks and crannies waiting to pop out when needed least. It is very important to ensure that all old abrasive is gone, because you now need to use a finer, 400 grade, abrasive in order to

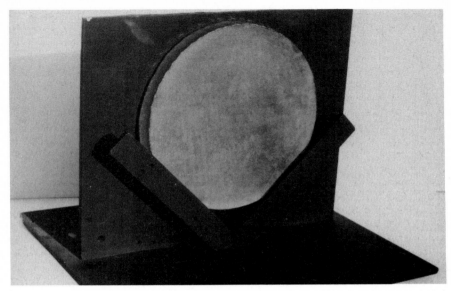

Figure 37. The mirror in a simple wooden stand for testing.

smooth out the surface ready for the first proper test of the true depth of curve we have achieved.

After grinding with the finer 400 grade abrasive for about three applications the surface will become much smoother and will take a thin film of water making it appear quite reflective. When wetted in this way stand the mirror on its edge, preferably in a simple wooden stand to stop it falling over as shown in Figure 37.

To test the curve use an ordinary torch and hold this to the side of your head, level with your right eye. Align yourself with the mirror in such a position that allows you to see the torch reflected in the mirror. If this reflection is the correct way up, you are inside the radius of curvature, if the reflection is inverted, you are outside the radius. Depending which side you are situated, move either closer to or further from the mirror until you come to a point where the reflection changes from an inverted to a correct one, or vice versa. This will prove a little difficult at first because around the critical point the mirror will seem to be filled with light. With patience and a few attempts a satisfactory position will be found that is the true radius of curvature. Measure this and half the distance is the focal length of your mirror.

If it is a good way out and you are a perfectionist you will probably wish to start again with rough grinding to obtain greater accuracy. If you are like me and are satisfied that the state of the mirror is good you will leave well alone and build the rest of the telescope to suit by simply adjusting the length of the tube. If you are satisfied you can now proceed to the next step.

Fine grinding

After the process of rough grinding you will see that the mirror is covered in pits and scratches which must now be removed completely before polishing can be undertaken. This is done by grinding with increasingly finer grades of abrasive. The idea is to reduce the sizes of the pits in the glass so they completely disappear in the final polishing process, but not to remove any more glass as the mirror is near the required shape.

Start your fine grinding with grade 120 abrasive (the 400 grade abrasive used at the end of rough grinding was just to allow the surface to retain water for testing). In the first stages of fine grinding it is pretty certain that some larger grains will be present in the grit which will tend to scratch, however, these should soon break down to become of no further trouble. Now a different stroke must be used. The stroke length should be of the shorter 1/3 stroke used in the intermediate stage of rough grinding and the same motion as that mentioned above can be used to good effect but a W shaped stroke will now be found more effective. The mirror is moved over the tool just under the 1/3 length stroke but in addition to this it should also be moved from a position having a 1 in (25 mm) overhang on the right to a position having a 1 in (25 mm) overhang on the left. This is where the W stroke gets its name. (See Figure 38.) In addition to this the action of rotating the mirror and moving bodily around the table, as with the rough grinding, should be continued.

You will be able to tell when the grinding effect of each charge of water and abrasive has ceased by the feel and sound. Do not carry on with each charge too long as nothing will be gained, only hard work for nothing. There will now be a tendency for mirror and tool to stick together, becoming quite difficult to part without damaging the mirror. If this does happen and the two

Figure 38. Diagram showing the motion required for the 'W' stroke.

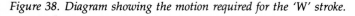

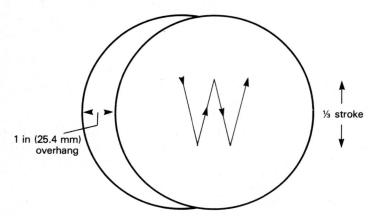

do become firmly stuck together, place them in warm water, they should then separate. If not and it becomes necessary to literally prise them apart, use only the edge of a piece of hardwood (and a prayer). Listen out carefully for the sound of splintering glass, get the cheque book out and start all over again.

When the grinding is judged to have less effect it will be noticed that the water and abrasive have now turned into a sort of sludge. This is a mixture of broken down abrasive and ground glass. Wash away this sludge and recharge with fresh water and abrasive. The period between each charge should be 5-10 minutes. It might also be advantageous to change the mirror/tool positions after each two charges, this should average out the overall effect on the mirror with the radius of curvature remaining unchanged.

After about one hour of continual grinding with 120 grade it should be time to move on to the next grade. This gradual reduction in grade should be carried out in similar intervals down to the final grade. The following table should give an indication of how long each stage should take and which grades to use.

Abrasive grade	Time	Number of charges
80 Carborundum	3 hours	As required
120 Carborundum	1 hour	10
220 Carborundum	1 hour	10
280 Carborundum	1 hour	10
400 Aloxite	1 hour	10
600 Aloxite	1 hour	10
1,000 Aloxite	45 minutes	8

Cerium oxide for polishing

As the grade becomes finer there will be an ever increasing tendency for mirror and tool to stick together and this can be exhausting and time consuming. By keeping fresh supplies of water and abrasive the situation will be easier. It also helps to add a little detergent to the water, this spreads the abrasive/water mixture over the mirror surface stopping the effect of clogging.

It becomes more important than ever, with the use of finer grades, that these do not become contaminated with coarser grade grit particles. Great care must be taken to remove every trace of the previous grade before commencing with the new one. To give an idea of just what can happen if when grinding with 600 grade a particle of 280 grade gets between the mirror and tool, it will only be removed by reverting back to 400 grade. No way can you ever get rid of scratches during polishing. No matter now small the scratch may be it would literally take years to remove. Though you may feel loath to do it, time will be saved in the end if you revert back to a previous grade.

One further point, during each stage check the bevel. As mentioned

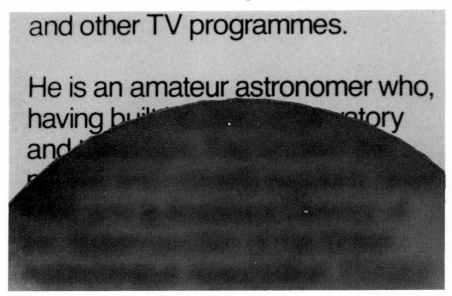

Figure 39. Close-up view of pits in the mirror surface following the first stage of fine grinding. The size of the pits should appear uniform before progressing to the next stage—checks should be made with a magnifying glass. Note the poor clarity of the glass when dry at this stage.

earlier any chips can spell disaster especially as one moves through the stages toward completion. Also check the pit sizes in the mirror's surface with a magnifying glass using a very strong light. If you are satisfied that all the pits are of the same size it is safe to move on to the next grade.

There is one more rule which should be observed. It is that if at any time you need to 'knock off' working for any time, no matter how short, do not leave mirror and tool in contact. If you do they will almost certainly become stuck. Always slide them apart before stopping for any reason.

If all has gone well at the end of the fine grinding you should be left with a spherical surface to the mirror, free from pits and scratches ready for the final polishing and figuring.

Testing the mirror

Before proceeding with the polishing there are two further things which must be done. One is to construct what is known as a Foucault tester. This allows tests to be made of the mirror's surface figure. Though amazingly simple to construct and seemingly rather crude, tests obtained with the instrument will be of astounding accuracy and the slightest irregularity will be made very obvious.

The Foucault tester uses a small point of light which is placed at the centre

Figure 40. Finding the radius of curvature with the Foucault tester. KE = knife edge, VP = viewing point, LS = light source.

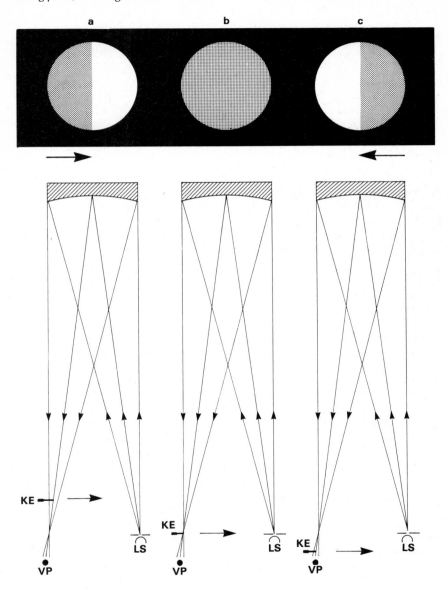

of curvature of the mirror. The light from this point source will strike the mirror surface evenly all over. If the surface is truly spherical all rays will be reflected back to the position of the source. If the source is then moved slightly to the right, but ensuring it is kept the same distance from the mirror, the point where the reflected light rays converge will be shifted slightly to the left. Place the eye in the position of convergence and if you are correctly placed the mirror will be seen to be filled with a faint light. This must of course be done in a fairly dark room so that this faint light reflected back from the mirror can be clearly seen.

If we now intersect the converging cone of light with a sharp edge, such as a knife, at a point just before it comes into focus, as this edge is moved into contact with the cone a shadow will be seen to move across the mirror in the same direction. If the knife edge is allowed to intersect the cone outside the point of focus this shadow will then move across the mirror in the opposite direction. If the blade were to intersect the cone at the exact point of focus then the light filling the mirror will be cut out instantly. If when this happens both light source and edge are equally distanced from the mirror, this will be an exact measure of the centre of the radius of curvature. If when the lights cuts off, the light source and edge distances are different, the centre of the radius of curvature is at a point exactly midway between the two. Whichever happens, the measure will be very accurate. If this distance is now halved the result will be the exact focal length of the mirror.

This is not the only purpose of the Foucault tester, however, it can also be used to show the true state of the mirror's surface. As already mentioned the mirror will be evenly filled with light if its figure is truly spherical. If, however, it is not, when the knife edge intersects the cone of light, the shadow will be seen to move unevenly across the mirror's surface causing shadows of various form. The shape of these shadows tells what state the surface of the mirror is in and shows up any hills, hollows, raised or depressed zones.

The pitch lap

The second thing you must do before starting polishing is to make what is known as a pitch lap with which you can actually polish the mirror's surface. The correct making and use of the lap are important in the obtaining of a high quality optical surface.

The pitch used in making the lap is itself of great importance. If very hard it will cause sleeks in the mirror's surface. These can probably better be described as tiny cuts rather than small scratches. If the pitch is not hard enough the edge of the mirror will dig into it. This will result in an imperfect figure with the mirror acquiring a turned down edge, about which more will be said later. There is a simple test for pitch hardness, just rest your hand with your thumb nail in contact with the pitch allowing only the weight of your hand to press the thumb nail into the pitch. Time how long it takes for a ¼ in (6 mm) dent to form in the pitch. If the time is less than twenty seconds the pitch is too soft, if over forty seconds it is too hard. If plate glass is used then 25 seconds is about right though harder pitch can be used on Pyrex or Duran 50.

The pitch can be hardened or softened quite easily. Melt the pitch in a saucepan then add turps drop by drop. Each time a drop or two has been added remove a little of the pitch, allow it to harden and use the thumbnail test until satisfied that it is just right, in this way it will be found that the pitch is gradually softened. To harden the pitch just heat carefully for prolonged periods. It must be pointed out that it is better if the pitch is a little too hard rather than a little too soft.

To make the lap itself heat the pitch in the pan. Immerse the mirror and tool into water, with a temperature of 100-150°F (38-66°C). Cut a band of wax paper and secure it around the edge of the tool with an elastic band, ensuring a slight overlap and a ¼ in (6 mm) projection above the edge of the tool (see Figure 41). Next make a mix of cerium oxide, water and soap. Use approximately one tablespoonful of cerium oxide, enough water to make it creamy and enough soap to make it feel slimy. The tool should then be placed on to a piece of baking foil. Spread a thin layer of turps over its upper surface with a paintbrush.

You are now ready to pour the hot pitch on to the tool. The pitch should not be boiling but must be quite molten. It is advisable to stir the pitch thoroughly before pouring. The pitch should be brought up to the level of the paper collar and should be poured in a spiral motion from the centre of the tool outward. After leaving to cool for 10-15 minutes the wax paper may be removed. The pitch should have stuck well to the tool because of the turps applied before pouring. In the meanwhile, when waiting for the pitch to cool, spread the creamy cerium oxide mixture on to the surface of the

Figure 41. Diagram showing the preparation of the tool for construction of a pitch lap.

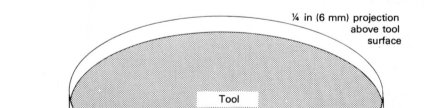

mirror. After removal of the paper, smear the surface of the pitch with the same cerium oxide mixture, being quite generous.

Next place the mirror face down on to the pitch lap. Move it around by small amounts to bed the pitch into the curve of the mirror's surface. The fit must be exact. When moving the mirror around slightly, make sure the edge of the glass does not dig into the pitch and spoil the fit. If it is found that the mirror and lap begin to stick together, slide the mirror slightly to expose a little of the lap and add more cerium oxide cream. Never separate the two during this process unless you are certain a good fit of the pitch to the mirror curve has been obtained. If it is removed it is impossible to replace it without air bubbles being trapped between the surfaces and these will spoil the fit by deforming the shape of the lap.

After about 45 minutes the pitch should have hardened sufficiently for safe removal of the mirror, though to be on the safe side it would not do any harm to leave it a little longer. Once the mirror is removed it is essential that the pitch is protected in some way without anything actually coming into contact with it. No dust should be allowed to settle on it, as this will cause scratching during the polishing. Ideally the lap should now be left for at least 12 hours, or if you have the time longer still.

The next job, when the lap is judged to be hardened sufficiently, is to trim all surplus pitch from around the edge with something like a Stanley knife which has been smeared with cerium oxide cream. This will allow it to cut much more cleanly. Now the pitch lap must be grooved in such a way as to enable polishing of the mirror by allowing the retention of the cerium oxide and water mixture during the polishing process. Also by cutting the grooves in a certain way it will determine the final shape of the mirror's surface.

Figure 42. Positioning the square facets of a pitch lap. The centre of the lap should be positioned toward the upper corner of one of the squares.

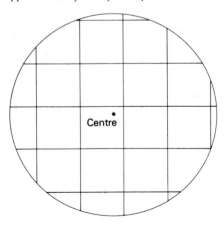

First mark the centre point of the pitch disc and draw a series of lines 1¼ in (32 mm) apart with a pencil and straight edge. Turn the lap through 90° and draw another series of lines to form 1¼ in (32 mm) squares as shown in Figure 42. Note also that the centre point must be situated in the corner of one of the squares. When marked off accurately, cut along these lines with a saw down to the surface of the glass tool, remembering to smear the saw with cerium oxide cream. This smearing with cerium oxide cream must always be done with anything used to cut the pitch as it stops snagging and ripping of the pitch. This will become most troublesome with the small portions of the squares near the edge of the tool. If care is not taken and the saw not well smeared, whole sections may be pulled out. You will certainly be able to congratulate yourself if you manage perfect results, so do not worry about small chips.

Next trim along these saw cuts, with the sharp Stanley knife, to make the cuts into V shaped grooves, which should have a total width of ¼ in (6 mm). After applying more cerium oxide cream to the mirror surface and lap, press the mirror on to the lap. Apply prolonged pressure by means of a weight resting on the mirror. A container with about one gallon of water left in place for about six hours should do the trick. After this period of 'cold pressing', a good contact between the two surfaces should have been achieved. If it is not satisfactory, place the pair into warm water, remove after a few minutes and smear the lap with cerium oxide. Then work the mirror over the lap until an even drag is felt, keep this up until it feels right. The pitch lap is now ready for the polishing process.

Lap moulds

Cutting the lap is not an easy job and it can be very messy. There is a way round this which some may prefer to experiment with. It involves the purchase of a rubber mould which can have either a square or hexagonal pattern.

If using the square grid mould continue with the construction of the lap as mentioned above up to the pouring of the hot pitch itself, but this time no wax paper collar will be needed. Place the rubber mould on to the mirror face and pour the molten pitch on to the mould. Place the tool face down on to the pitch, invert the lot and work the mirror over the pitch until the mould shows through. This will be visible through the mirror. The main problem with this is the outer square facets will lose pitch and will not stand as high as the rest. It may therefore, be necessary to build them up with more hot pitch. Then continue as before by pressing the lap into shape against the mirror surface under weight after removing the mould. Remember, when separating the lap and the mirror always slide them apart, and use plenty of cerium oxide cream to prevent them sticking together.

The hexagonal faceted rubber mould is easier to use but is really only suitable for small diameter mirrors. It would however, be perfect for a

Figure 43. A button lap with the rubber mould used to form it. This type is suitable for smaller mirrors.

mirror of the size we are concerned with here, and I would suggest you use this type, constructing the lap in the above-mentioned way.

Polishing

The idea now is to get as smooth a surface as possible, free from all scratches and pits. You must concentrate on surface deformities such as hills or hollows etc. The latter may take many forms, but however slight they may be they must be removed if your mirror is to be classed as a good one. At this point it must be said that reasonable results can be obtained with mirrors which are less than perfect, as born out by the fact that many mirrors churned out by some manufacturers are substandard, yet people use them and find them tolerable. It is not until one has compared the view given by a substandard mirror to one which is near perfect, that the latter's value is appreciated. If you are going to the trouble of making your own mirror then you might as well get it right. The sense of pride in achieving perfection is great indeed—the added bonus of a superb view will make it all the more worthwhile.

One of the most troublesome aspects of the mirror polishing process is the need to sustain a constant temperature and a virtually dust-free environment in the room where it is to be done. Testing mirrors at various times during polishing, when temperatures have been allowed to change will cause the mirror to show an apparently different figure. The result being that unnecessary work will be carried out. The ideal temperature is around 68°F (20°C). The control of this is not so important when only trying to smooth out the surface, but later, when trying to get rid of errors in the figure it is vital.

The polishing agent should be a solution of one part of cerium oxide to three parts of water, which can be kept in a small squeezy bottle. Squirt a fair amount of the solution on to the lap, then place the mirror face down and work it around to ensure the solution is spread over the whole lap. Then using the W stroke described earlier polish for approximately 30 minutes at a speed which allows one complete W stroke each minute, all the while keeping up a good supply of polishing solution. The reason the strokes must be carried out quite slowly is that speedy strokes will cause the lap to heat up and distort. If such problems arise and you feel the process is not going correctly, stop to allow cooling of the mirror and lap and press as before under a weight. It is advisable to do this after each half hour spell, in any case. It will also be necessary to clean out the lap grooves with a knife every so often to stop them clogging or closing up.

To completely polish out all pits will take several hours. It may well look shiny long before this but close inspection will reveal that many tiny pits remain. Do not expect to polish for a period much shorter than eight hours. If during this period you need to leave to have a rest, slide mirror and tool apart and protect them from falling dust. After this period the time will be right for the testing of the mirror surface with the Foucault tester, to see just how good (or bad) it is. To look at, the mirror will seem perfect, the Foucault test will show its true worth, however. The highly reflective surface of the mirror now means that the test can be carried out without the need to wet the mirror surface.

Final testing

The mirror should now be tested exactly at the centre of the radius of curvature. By use of the light and dark shades which occur as a sharp edge (or knife edge as it is referred to) is brought into contact with the converging light rays from the mirror, the mirror's true form can be examined. This was mentioned briefly in the earlier section on the Foucault tester, but just what different shades tell us needs now to be discussed in more detail.

If perfectly spherical, which it should now be, the mirror will appear evenly illuminated over its whole surface. When the knife edge is introduced at the point exactly at the radius of curvature it will darken gradually all over. If there are irregularities it will not darken evenly and unless you are either very lucky, or very skilful, your first attempt will show considerable unevenness of shading.

What this unevenness amounts to is that any deviation from a spherical figure will cause light rays from the point source to be reflected back in other directions which are governed by the angle of the region the light hits. So the knife edge will cut off some of the rays but not others. Some parts of the mirror will therefore appear in shadow, other parts will appear bright and some parts will appear intermediate. The effect is really obvious even though the irregularities being measured are very small indeed. Holes and hills will look a thousand times deeper or higher than they really are, so an error only one millionth of an inch (.000025 mm) will show up as though it were $^1/_{10}$ in (2.5 mm). It will however, have the same dimensions of width.

Place the knife edge so that it intersects the light cone from the left, with a light to the right. Irregularities in the mirror will seem to be illuminated by light from the right of the mirror. Therefore, a hump in the mirror will have a shadow to its left. Depressions will show the reverse. They are of course not real shadows cast by the irregularities, but only appear so. They do high-light the type of defect we have to deal with.

Though I have said that these irregularities are very small, make no mis-take, they will severely effect the performance of your mirror if not cor-rected. What is now required is the flat illumination of a spherical surface. Once we have achieved this we can move on to parabolize the mirror, give it the parabolic figure that it must have to perform the function required of it.

One other type of test worthy of mention here is known as the Ronchi test. With this, instead of the knife edge, a grating is used which should consist of about a hundred lines to the inch (25 mm). Each line therefore being $^1/_{100}$ in (¼ mm) apart. Though they can be made it is rather fiddly and far easier to purchase one. Replace the knife edge with the grating using a narrow slit for the light source, ensuring that the slit is parallel to the Ronchi lines. The mirror when viewed from the regular position will now appear covered by a series of narrow dark and bright lines. The lines should not bend if the mirror is spherical. Any bending of the lines indicates irregularities of the mirror surface.

In order that an evaluation can be made of the various shadow forms and what is to be learned from them, the next chapter contains descriptions of the more common forms likely to be encountered.

Chapter 11

Mirror irregularities and their correction

Spherical
If the mirror shows this figure then it is perfect and the next stage can be commenced. More than likely it will not be spherical at the first test. Figure 44 shows the shape of lines and state of shading you must aim for.

Turned-down edge
This is best shown by the Ronchi test, where the lines will curve inward at the edge. However, with the Foucault test a perfect mirror should show a bright thin line all around its edge and this brightness at the rim should be just a little brighter on the right when tested at the centre of the radius of curvature. If the bright rim is absent from the left-hand side, with a tendency for that part to be shaded, the mirror has a turned-down edge.

The way to get rid of this is to polish, using short strokes about a third to a quarter of the mirror diameter in length, and of the normal back and forth

Figure 44. Spherical pattern. In all these diagrams the Ronchi patterns are shown with the screen inside the focus and the Foucault patterns are shown with the light source to the right.

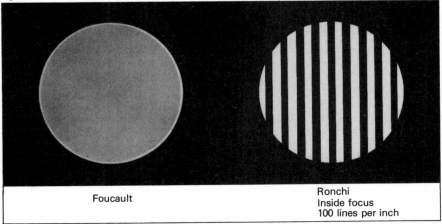

| Foucault | Ronchi
Inside focus
100 lines per inch |

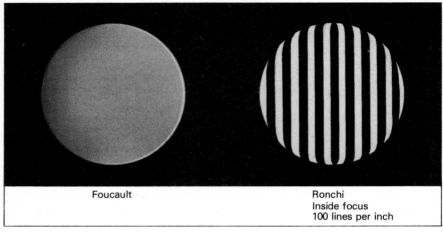

Figure 45. *Turned-down edge.*

type. Make a check after each 5 minute spell until removed. If the turned-down edge is very bad then a return to fine grinding will be necessary.

Turned-up edge
If when the Foucault tester is used the above-mentioned bright rim has a tendency to be brighter on the left, the edge is turned up. The Ronchi bands will appear to curve outward from the vertical axis as they reach the rim, opposite in fact to the effect of a turned-down edge.

Short 5 minute periods of polishing using longer strokes should put

Figure 46. *Turned-up edge.*

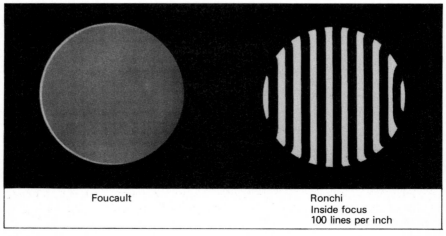

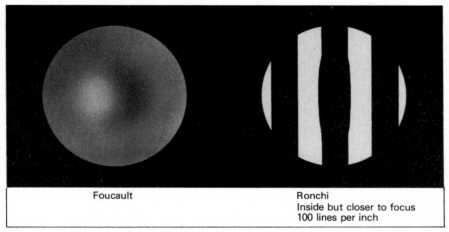

| Foucault | Ronchi
Inside but closer to focus
100 lines per inch |

Figure 47. Central depression.

matters right. If things do not improve after a short while the chances are that you will produce a hollow in the centre of the mirror. Invert the mirror/lap positions and very carefully polish so that the centre of the lap is over the edge of the mirror. Watch out though, as you may reverse the situation, ending up with a turned-down edge.

Central depression
This may be remedied by using short one third diameter strokes. If not, modification to the lap may be necessary. This is done simply by cold pressing the lap with a circle of wax paper placed in the area of the depression in the mirror, cut to the same size. This reduces contact of the lap with the glass in the offending area allowing only the surrounding regions to be polished. Unless the depression is really bad this should work very quickly. Such deformation of the main lap is disliked by many and it may be better to treat this problem by use of the sub-diameter lap to be described later. In the case of the depressed centre, use the lap with short elliptical strokes over the higher areas surrounding the depressions, returning to normal back and forward motion as the depression becomes less obvious. It will be very quickly effective and tests should be made regularly.

Raised centre
This can be remedied by lengthening the polishing stroke with the regular-sized lap though in this way a turned edge might be the outcome. A slight modification of a normal stroke could help. Here the mirror overhangs the lap, the normal back and forth movement is then used, while walking round as usual (see Figure 48). It will rectify things very quickly but may well produce a depression.

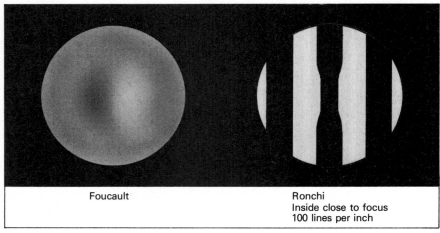

| Foucault | Ronchi
Inside close to focus
100 lines per inch |

Figure 48. Raised centre.

Deformation of the main lap is another way. In this case a ring instead of a disc is cut and the lap cold pressed with this in place. This will have the effect of raising the central area of the lap slightly, though again for reasons mentioned above this is disliked by many. Once more a sub-diameter lap will be preferred, working this over the raised area only. Remember, here, as with any attempt to rectify deformities, regular checks are essential. It is so easy to go too far and cause other problems, even reversing the original situation completely.

Figure 49. Raised ring.

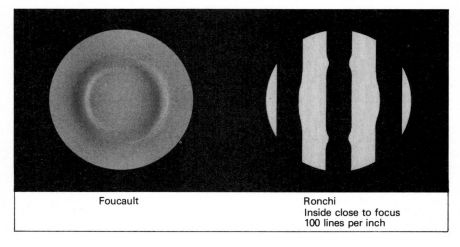

| Foucault | Ronchi
Inside close to focus
100 lines per inch |

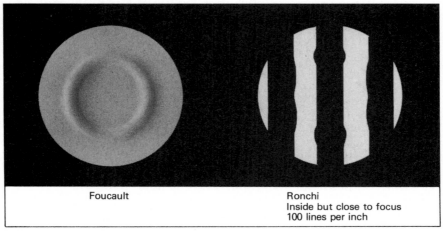

| Foucault | Ronchi
Inside but close to focus
100 lines per inch |

Figure 50. Depressed ring.

Raised ring
The best treatment for this is slightly elliptical side strokes or figure of eight strokes, though such action usually can produce a turned-down edge. It might be worth that risk though, because the latter if not too severe is easier to rectify than the raised ring.

It is likely that the raised ring results from a poorly made lap, with facets not positioned properly. (Remember the need for positioning of the squares off centre?) The facets of the lap may also be uneven in height. In the case of the former the only answer is to make a fresh lap, if the latter is the case re-formation of the lap by the cold pressing method should suffice.

Depressed ring
This is not so easy to remedy. Perhaps the best way to try to deal with it is to work on the raised areas around the depressed ring with a sub-diameter lap, checking even more regularly which way things are going because they can easily go very wrong.

Dog biscuit
When viewed with the Foucault tester, the mirror may show a very uneven surface. This will have been caused by periods of polishing which have been too prolonged or carried out too quickly. Heat build-up will have distorted the lap facets and possibly caused parts of the mirror to expand. The result is a very bumpy surface. It is best to try to avoid this rather than have to attempt to correct it. If, when testing, the mirror shows this tendency, slow down the strokes.

The effect could be confused with two other problems. If the air in the room where the Foucault test is done is not too steady, the pattern on the

Foucault

Figure 51. Dog biscuit effect as seen during the Foucault test.

mirror will appear very uneven. By continuing to watch the shades on the mirror it will be noticed that they are in motion and this is certainly caused as currents of air pass between you and the mirror. Wait until the air is very still before making a judgement. A hand placed near the mirror by a second person will show the air movement effect vividly. It is an experiment well worth while trying in order to familiarize yourself with the effect caused by moving air currents.

A second effect is one in which the mirror will resemble the surface of orange peel. Though this may look bad it is not too much of a problem, and may not affect too badly the performance of the mirror. It could be the result of overheating of the lap or it might be due to numerous tiny pits in the mirror's surface, these being so tiny that they escaped detection prior to this test. Fine grinding should be returned to otherwise one might be tempted to live with it.

*   *   *

It may not be easy to work out just what the shadings or Ronchi lines show. Sometimes the mirror may show any combination of the above defects. In fact rarely is just one defect seen to stand out clearly on its own. To sort out just what that combination is can be very difficult. Even when the combination has been decoded as it were, there is still the problem of deciding which action to take and whether that action, while solving one problem will not increase another. Don't be put off by these difficulties, just be aware of them. It is possible to correct things eventually.

The sub-diameter lap
Some of the defects just described could be worked upon by deformation of the regular lap as mentioned already. Many people prefer not to do this

since it might happen that the lap could be required later to remedy defects of another type. Continually deforming and re-forming the lap could lead to further problems.

An alternative method is to make what is called a sub-diameter lap. This can then be used to work directly on certain areas of the mirror. To make such a lap, cut a circular plywood base about two thirds the diameter of the mirror, then seal or varnish it. As with the tool of the main lap this should be covered on one side with pitch and facets cut in the way described previously. These should be around ¾ in (18 mm) square. Press against the mirror as with the original lap.

Sub-diameter laps usually act on deformities quickly thus saving time. They are convenient because they allow the form of the main lap to remain unchanged.

Chapter 12

Parabolizing

Assuming that a good spherical figure has now been achieved, the next step is to change the form of the mirror's figure from part of a sphere to a deeper parabolic curve. When performing the Foucault test a certain type of shadow pattern is to be looked for. Certain zones of the mirror must now be tested by using various knife edge settings. It must be said that this part of the mirror making can be the most difficult of all.

The parabola differs from a spherical surface in that it deepens toward the centre while straightening out toward the edges. To achieve this curve the lap needs to be modified. The facets of the lap must be made gradually smaller as they approach the outer edge. This is done by simply widening the grooves between the facets toward the edge of the lap (see Figure 62).

If this is done and good contact between mirror and lap ensured, then a small number of short polishing strokes should enable you to gain the

Figure 52. Diagram to show how a lap should be modified for parabolizing.

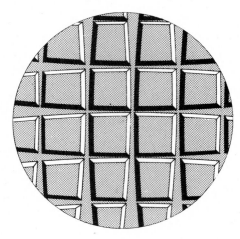

required curve. Spells of polishing should be very short now. At least half an hour should be allowed to elapse between the last polishing stroke and the testing. This will allow the mirror to cool. What we are now dealing with is a very small measurement indeed. There are many things which can fool us into the wrong conclusion. The actual temperature of the mirror does not really matter, only that the temperature is even over the whole mirror. The figure will be grossly distorted if it is not.

When it is felt that a paraboloid surface has been achieved, tests must now be made on various parts of the mirror's curve. This is where things become a little complicated. The parabolic form which we are after means that the rays of light reflected back by the mirror do not come together at the same point, just as with the deformities, but now in a controlled fashion. Those from the centre of the mirror will focus closer to the mirror itself, while those from the edge will be brought to focus further from it. The amount of difference depends on the ratio of focal length to mirror diameter and can be expressed thus:

$$\frac{r^2}{R}$$

r = radius of zone to be tested
R = radius of curvature of mirror
  eg for our 6 in (152 mm) mirror of 48 in (120 cm) f1 we have a 3 in (76 mm) radius and a 96 in (240 cm) radius of curvature.

$$\text{So} \quad \frac{r^2}{R} = \frac{9}{96} = \frac{3}{32}$$

This only applies if the knife edge is moved independently of the light source. If not $r^2/2R$ should be used.

When tested at the radius of curvature, therefore, the rays from the mirror's centre should come to a focus $^3/_{32}$ in (2.3 mm) nearer to the mirror than the rays from the edge. Therefore it should be possible to find a point at which, when the knife edge is brought into contact with the converging rays, the edge of the mirror only will be seen to darken. Then, by moving the knife edge toward the mirror by $^3/_{32}$ in (2.3 mm) only the centre should darken evenly. If this effect occurs with less movement of the knife edge we have not achieved the parabola we require, so more polishing is needed. If the amount moved is greater than $^3/_{32}$ in (2.3 mm) we have a hyperbolic curve which is in effect too deep.

More zones than the two mentioned above should be tested so that it can be assessed whether the parabolic curve required is true for the whole surface of the mirror. The graph given in Figure 53 shows what the curve of the mirror should be if tested at three zones. The central curve is in theory a perfect mirror. The lines either side indicate the permitted deviation from the perfect curve. If you end up with a curve that wholly fits within these lines the mirror can be regarded as quite respectable. Obviously the closer the curve is to the central line the better.

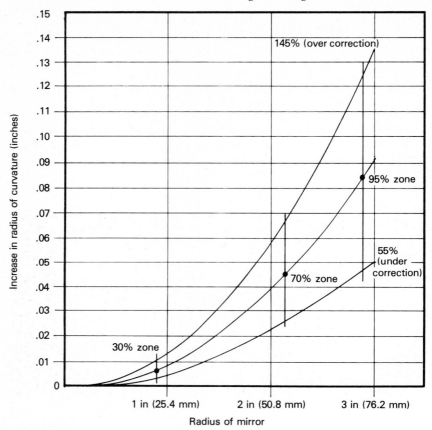

Figure 53. Graph (a) shows a perfect parabolic curve for a 6 in (15 cm) f8 mirror. Graphs (b) and (c) show the acceptable limits into which a mirror's curve must fall if it is to be of reasonable quality.

The various zones to be tested could be marked on the mirror with wax and used to indicate the part of the mirror under test. As a guide, the positions for the various zones to be tested on a 6 in (152 mm) f8 mirror are as follows:

Zone	Distance from mirror centre	Knife edge movement
30 per cent	0.9 in (22.86 mm)	.0084 in (8.4 thou)
75 per cent	2.1 in (53.34 mm)	.046 in (46 thou)
95 per cent	2.85 in (72.39 mm)	.085 in (85 thou)

Generally it is felt that a slightly under-corrected mirror, or one that is a little shallow, is better than a mirror which is over-corrected, or too deep. With a plate glass mirror the continual drop in night time temperature will tend to correct a shallow curve, whereas a mirror already too deep will deepen still further so that sharp images will not be possible. If it has been found that the curve is over-corrected simply recut the grooves of the lap making the central facets smaller than those at the edge. This will reverse the parabolizing effect. Short type strokes should be used.

When the final test is to be made to check the parabola, it is wise to leave the mirror for at least two hours. This should allow the temperature of the glass to settle down.

Figure 54. Four illustrations showing the pattern of a parabolic mirror when the Foucault test and Ronchi test are used.

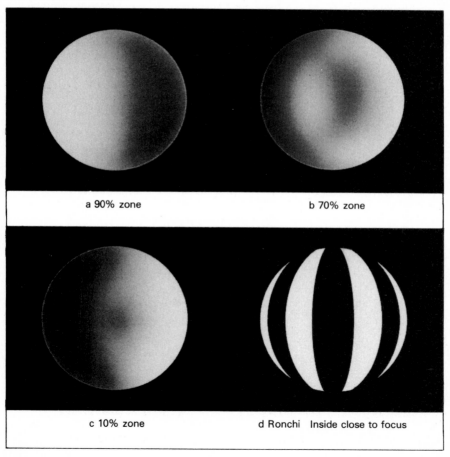

a 90% zone   b 70% zone

c 10% zone   d Ronchi   Inside close to focus

Chapter 13

The secondary

Once you have a good parabolic mirror the job of completing the optical parts for the instrument is far from finished. There is another major component required for the Newtonian, this being a secondary mirror, which could be an elliptical flat, or, if preferred, a prism, used to deflect the converging beam.

The prism secondary is really only practical for smaller-sized instruments and a 6 in (152 mm) reflector is, in my view, rather over the limit. These can easily be purchased from most optical firms. If one of these is to be used it must be judged at what point the rays of light are to be intersected. Also it must be ensured that the prism is large enough to enable the whole mirror to be seen reflected in it when viewed at the eyepiece position. Yet it must not be so big as to show a large part of the inside of the tube. Both situations will result in light loss. Because the prism appears square when viewed at the required angle, the result is that a considerable area of the prism is not in use. This means that some of the incoming light is stopped, again reducing light grasp. For this reason prisms are not favoured, especially for larger instruments.

In the case of an elliptical flat secondary, the appearance of which is circular when viewed at the required angle, its size can be such that there is little or no wasted area and therefore no light loss through a greater than necessary obstruction. It is more expensive than the prism, however. Also the prism has no coated surface to deteriorate. But these advantages are largely cancelled out by the greater obstructed area. So for the purpose of the telescope described in this book I would recommend the elliptical flat.

You do not wish to spoil the quality of the image produced by the primary mirror with the secondary, so its surface must be perfectly flat. Its function is simply to deflect the convergent beam without changing it. Many people do not appreciate the importance of this part of the telescope, but if the flat is not a good one, all the work spent ensuring the mirror was of excellent figure was a waste of time. All of the light reflected back by the primary passes off the flat, so it must have a surface of equal quality in its own way.

The first thing to do is to find out what size a flat needs to be for a given mirror. To do this we must adopt the following formula:

$$d = \frac{rD + f'X}{F}$$

where

d = the minor axis of the diagonal flat's elliptical shape
r = the distance from the axis of the tube to the ocular field lens
D = the diameter of the mirror
F' = the focal length of the mirror less the distance r
F = the focal length of the mirror in total
X = diameter of the field lens of the eyepiece. This is not constant with all eyepieces so it should be taken as being ⅞ in (22 mm).

For a 6 in (152 mm) f8, ideally the tube should be at least 7 in (178 mm) in diameter. If you wish your eyepiece field lens to be say 1½ in (38 mm) outside the tube wall, you should then be able, by use of the formula, to arrive at a figure for your diagonal minor axis.

$$\frac{(5 \times 6) + (43 \times 7/8)}{48} = 1.4 \text{ in}$$

So the minor axis of the diagonal should be 1.4 in (36 mm).

The diagonal must of course be elliptical in shape so that when viewed at a 45° angle it appears circular. Therefore to find the major axis multiply 1.4 by 1.42. This gives 2.13 in (54 mm). If photography with the telescope is proposed, more clearance than 1½ in (38 mm) beyond the tube may be necessary. This can be taken into account with the above formula.

Having sorted this out, the simplest way would be to purchase a diagonal from a reputed dealer. If however, having produced a masterpiece of a mirror you would not feel happy for it to be used with anyone's flat but your own, then how should you go about making one? A point should be borne in mind here. To test a diagonal for flatness ideally requires another flat, so my advice is to purchase one in the first place. There is however, the distinct possibility that you will go on to make more than one telescope, so this is how to do it.

First purchase a piece of plate glass (about 14 in (36 cm) square for a 6 in reflector) from a dealer and cut this into three rectangles, measuring just over 1½ in (38 mm) by 2¼ in (57 mm). This will probably best be done by the glazier, though you may prefer to do it in order to avoid damage to the glass surface. With a great deal of luck it might just happen that one of the pieces may have a surface flat enough for your purpose. There is a simple way to test for flatness. This is to press two of the pieces of glass together, ensuring they are both clean and dry. If light reflected from the two surfaces in contact is viewed obliquely (at a slant or angle) an interference pattern known as Newton's rings will be seen. If these coloured bands are circular or sharply curved, then the surfaces are not perfectly flat but either slightly convex or concave. Keep trying the various surfaces of the pieces together until you find two that show either straight or nearly straight bands. The less the lines curve the flatter will be the surfaces. A way to see these bands better is to view them under monochromatic light. That emitted by a sodium vapour light will show it best, the bands being sharply contrasted in yellow and black. It will be far easier to measure these to assess the degree of flatness of the surfaces.

You might be fortunate enough to find a surface which will be good enough to use as a diagonal without any further work needed. If not it will be necessary to work the best surface by fine grinding and polishing, similar to that done when in the final stages of making the primary. To do this it is best to follow a certain procedure. Also it is advisable to make two diagonals at the same time, giving the opportunity to choose the best of the two, plus having a replacement, in case one gets damaged, or even a test flat should you wish to go into production. They can also of course be tested against each other later. Next cut some more pieces of the plate glass in such shapes that they loosely fit together to form a rough circle with the two pieces chosen for the diagonals in the centre (see Figure 55).

Once you have found the flattest surfaces of the two chosen, mark the backs to ensure they are placed best face up for polishing. Two other pieces of glass will also be needed. One should be about 6 in (152 mm) square, the other 8 in (203 mm) square. These could all be cut from the original piece of plate.

Figure 55. Positions in which to place pieces of glass when making the diagonal—(a) and (b) will be the actual pieces used.

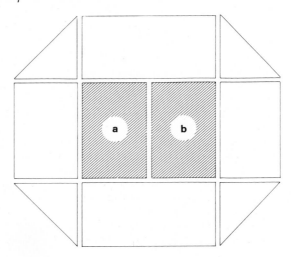

Bevel all edges of the glass slightly, then wash them all thoroughly. Smear hot paraffin wax on one face of the 6 sq in piece and place the diagonals together with the other pieces on to this as shown in Figure 55, leaving gaps between them approximately $^1/_{16}$ in (1.5 mm) wide. Fill these gaps afterwards with more paraffin wax.

Now using the table originally used for making the mirror, place the 8 sq in piece of glass on to it. Sprinkle a solution of water and 400 grade abrasive over the glass, then place the 6 in piece with the diagonals attached face down and proceed to grind, using the W stroke. Do not allow the upper 6 in (152 mm) piece to overhang the lower, as this will affect the final flatness of the diagonals. Continue grinding for a period which requires at least a dozen changes of fresh abrasive solution. After this period wash thoroughly and clean out the gaps. Replace this with fresh paraffin wax. If any old abrasive is left, by now you should know what will happen! Continue as before with 600 grade and finally 1,000 grade giving each a comparable time and cleaning well between each stage.

Next a piece of plywood cut to an 8 in diameter circle is needed. It should be well varnished. This is for a new pitch lap which should be cast in the same way as the original mirror lap, using a wax paper collar and pouring the hot pitch to a depth of about ¼ in (6 mm). When the lap has cooled, press the pitch against the ground surface of the 8 in square piece of glass using the polishing agent cream again, as with the mirror lap. Ideally a fine plastic mesh should also be used to press into the surface of the lap in order to leave an impression of the mesh and assist in polishing. Incidentally, this method can also be used for the mirror itself and it does speed up the polishing process, though it is not essential.

Commence polishing with the glass over the lap, using cerium oxide solution, for a period of half an hour, employing W strokes. Continue this for 30 minute spells, each time reversing the glass/lap position in order to retain flatness, and until thoroughly polished. Finally, remove and test the diagonals, choosing the best of the two.

Cutting the diagonal to shape

Cutting the diagonal into the required ellipse is the next stage. The least sophisticated way of doing this is to take one of them and cut off the corners. Next cut a piece of gummed paper to the size and shape of the ellipse required then stick it to the glass. The idea then is to very carefully nibble off the surplus glass with a pair of pliers. It is fraught with danger. One false move and your nice flat diagonal will have a great chip in it. . . to put it mildly, I would not recommend it.

Assuming the risk was taken and most of the surplus glass has been chipped away successfully, fix a piece of ordinary glass to each side of the diagonal, using a thin layer of pitch. Fix the whole glass sandwich to a turning spindle which has its end cut to 45°, warming the glass slightly before fixing, and again using pitch as an adhesive. When fixed rotate the spindle and centralize it while the pitch is still warm. If a lathe is available, so much the better, but I find an old hand-cranked grinding wheel attachment ideal.

Next find a piece of tubing, the inside diameter of which is close to the required minor axis of the diagonal. Cut the tube down its length so that it can be opened out to fit over the glass sandwich in its present state. Pour into this tube a solution of coarse abrasive (120 grade), slip this over the glass while spinning and apply light pressure, squeezing on the tube with one hand while cranking with the other. Fresh abrasive should be added continually for this will help in grinding down the edge more quickly. When the edge is nearly ground down use a finer abrasive, say 200 grade. This will do to finish off with. When the gap in the tube closes up the process is complete.

After disconnecting the diagonal, remove the two pieces of protective glass and remove the pitch with turps. To finish off with bevel the edges of the diagonal as with the primary mirror, but only a small bevel is required in this case.

Perhaps a better way of shaping the diagonal is to use a biscuit cutter. Though slightly more involved, it is far safer. Make a small plywood box of such a size that when the diagonal is placed into it the angle at which it lies is 45°. If necessary it could be held in place by small cleats, but if made correctly it should fit in fairly snugly. Again as with the last method the diagonal should be sandwiched between two pieces of protective glass. To protect the diagonal even further, fill the box with plaster of Paris and allow to dry for at least a day.

The cutter itself could be made from a piece of stainless steel tube with an inside diameter slightly larger than the required diagonal minor axis. The end of the tube should be plugged with hardwood or a piece of steel if possible. The centre of this plug should be drilled and a steel shaft of approximately ¼ in (6 mm) diameter inserted. This should be fixed by a small bolt running through the tube plug and shaft. This should secure the arrangement. Drill a couple of small holes in the tube beneath the plug for ventilation and serrate the bottom rim of the tube which is to be the cutting edge. Insert the shaft of the whole arrangement into the chuck of an upright drill, ensuring that it is centred. If you have not got one yourself, make friends with someone who has, or even rent one.

Set the drill to a slow speed of approximately 150 rpm. Clamp the box containing the diagonal to the drill platform and centre it. Provided you have arranged things just right the cutter should go through the glass just where you want it to. Use a solution of 120 grade abrasive and start to cut carefully, stopping frequently after each few minutes to allow things to cool. Do not proceed too fast, apart from risking shattering the diagonal, the cut will not be a good one, it will splay out, the end result giving a greater size to one side of the diagonal than the other.

If all goes smoothly remove the protective glass as before and bevel the front edge.

Right *An 8½ in (21.5 cm) Dobsonian, one of the most simple and effective altazimuth designs. It can be built largely from wood and made to look very attractive.*

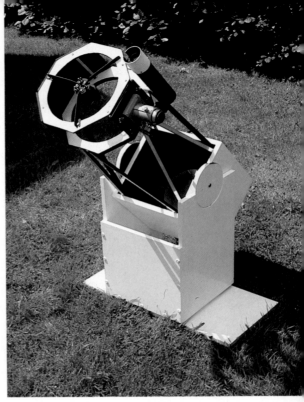

Below *All that remains of Herschel's 40 ft reflector on show in the grounds of the Old Greenwich Observatory.*

Above *One side of the base frame of a fork mount for a 16½ in (42 cm) reflector. This view shows one of the steel rollers held by two plumber block bearings.*

Left *Another view of the same base frame showing how the main fork and polar axis flywheel rides between the base rollers.*

Above *Photograph of a four-vane spider, showing the use of very broad vanes for greater stability. These can be narrow enough so as not to cause excessive light loss. Note that by offsetting the four vanes, so that they do not meet at a common centre, stability is further improved by cutting down on vibration.*

Right *An octagonal wooden tube with open sections and plywood baffles of the type shown in the square tube construction. The design works particularly well, being strong and relatively free from tube currents. In this case the tube has a rotating upper section to make the eyepiece easily accessible whatever the position of the telescope. For this idea to work properly the rotating section must be accurately made so as not to upset alignment of the optical train when it is rotated.*

Above *A run off shed open.*

Left *A small domed observatory housing an 8 in (20 cm) reflector with part of the hatch removed for viewing. The whole structure is of plywood and hardboard, looking very attractive and unobtrusive in garden surroundings.*

Chapter 14

Coating the mirrors

When happy that the mirror and diagonal are satisfactory, they must next receive a coating to make their surfaces highly reflective. There are two popular ways in which this coating can be applied, one being a silver coating, deposited chemically, the other an aluminium film, deposited by evaporation in a vacuum chamber. The latter form of coating must be done by a firm with expensive, specialist equipment. Of the two, aluminizing gives the harder coating which is more resistant to atmospheric pollution and damp.

With proper care an aluminium coating can last several years. It is even possible to have a double coating to which can be applied a protective film of material, such as silicon dioxide. This again must be done by experts and incurs only a little more expense. Some do not like this idea for they feel it degrades the image slightly. It also renders an old aluminium coating difficult to remove in readiness for a fresh application. Also pinholes in the overcoat can allow damp to penetrate, marking the aluminium film.

In reality these problems are far outweighed by the fact that the coating lasts so much longer, a certain percentage of reflectivity being sustained for periods well in excess of coatings not so protected.

The actual reflectivity of an aluminium coating amounts to at most about 88 per cent which is not as efficient as a freshly silvered mirror. This can have a reflectivity as high as 93 per cent in the beginning. That fact together with its much lower cost in the past led many people to prefer it. The main problem is that the silver coating does not last so long. It is readily tarnished by atmospheric pollution and much more seriously affected by water or damp. Unless you are in a position to silver a mirror regularly, say once every six months, the initial advantage of higher reflectivity is soon lost. Heavily polluted air can result in losses of 10 per cent, or even 20 per cent, over just a few weeks. This loss can be even worse for those wishing to use the instrument for photography, with a reduction of as much as 50 per cent in actinic wavelengths.

The speed with which a silver coating deteriorates is very much dependent on conditions around the observatory. Factories, smoking chimneys or sites near the sea being major problems. The life of a silver coating will be considerably lengthened if the observatory is situated well away from all of these. This also applies of course to aluminium coatings though to a lesser extent. I managed, with care, to retain a good aluminium film for six years in the heart of Stoke on Trent, with two years for a silvered mirror at a site in South Cheshire. However, to put this into perspective, at the same Cheshire site, an aluminium coating applied to a 16½ in (419 mm) mirror in 1978 remained good until 1985 and would probably have lasted a few years longer had it not proved necessary to modify the figure of the mirror.

Silvering

As mentioned there are many things which tip the balance of favour toward aluminizing these days. Many books will ignore the process of silvering, saying that the price of chemicals makes it too costly. They even go so far as to say that the chemicals required can no longer be obtained. On balance, it has to be admitted that aluminizing is perhaps the better choice but so far as cost is concerned it is marginal. There is the satisfaction of coating your own mirror to be gained which is rather akin to developing your own photographs. It may not be cheaper these days, but at least you are in control of the quality. As to the availability of the chemicals, well to say they are unobtainable is going a little too far. Any respectable chemist, provided assurance can be given that the reason for wanting the chemicals is a bona fide one, will supply them. Most of them are very cheap indeed, it is the price of silver nitrate which has increased so much lately that causes a problem.

For those of you who are in a position to silver your own mirror a step by step guide follows. There are many different methods for doing this. The one given here was described to the author by a chemist many years ago. It is simple and has proved very successful. The process is based on the fact that ammoniacal solution of silver oxide is reduced to the metal by various substances such as glucose.

By carefully controlling the temperature and the concentration of solutions, together with extreme cleanliness, it will be possible to deposit the silver as a film to give a mirror surface.

The following quantities will be required for a 6 in (152 mm) mirror:
Silver nitrate ½ oz (12.5 g) dissolved in 8 fl oz (227 ml) of distilled water.
Sodium (or potassium) hydroxide pure ¼ oz (6.25 g) dissolved in 8 fl oz (227 ml) of distilled water.
Glucose powder 1 oz (25 g) dissolved in 8 fl ozs (227 ml) of distilled water.
Ammonia solution SG 880 2 fl oz (5 ml).
Nitric acid pure 70 per cent 2 oz (50 g).
Optical rouge
Distilled water 4 pints (2.23 litres).

Take a glass or earthenware dish of slightly larger diameter than the mirror. The dish and mirror must be thoroughly cleaned with a pure soap powder such as Dreft, then rinsed well with water. Next clean with strong nitric acid, using a wad of cotton wool on a stick or stirring rod. Great care must be taken to avoid splashing and contact of the acid with the skin.

Rinse the mirror well with distilled water and on no account touch the surface to be silvered. If the mirror is well cleaned it should hold a film of water. If water is repelled by any part of the surface it is not clean enough, and it should again be cleaned with nitric acid. If satisfied that the mirror is clean enough, pour sufficient distilled water into the dish so as to just cover the mirror.

Put the silver nitrate solution into a glass container with a capacity of about 1 pt (568 ml). This should also have been cleaned in the same way as the mirror and dish. Add ¼ fl oz (7.1 ml) of ammonia solution. This will produce a brown precipitate of silver oxide which is soluble in excess of ammonia. Add more ammonia, a few drops at a time stirring constantly. As soon as clearing of the solution appears imminent, add the ammonia drop by drop until the solution just clears.

Next add 8 fl oz (227 ml) of sodium hydroxide solution. This causes a further brown precipitate. Add further ammonia solution until a point is reached where the solution is clear, except for dark suspended specks. Do not try to dissolve these as this would lead to excess of ammonia.

Then add 2 fl oz (5 ml) of the glucose solution and pour over the mirror in the dish. The temperature of the solutions should be between 55°F (12.8°C) and 65°F (18.3°C). Now rock gently. The silver coating will be seen to gradually form.

After about 5 minutes the surface may be gently swabbed with cotton wool, to keep the floccules of silver which float in the solution on the move. After 8-10 minutes, examine the mirror every so often by tilting the dish and remove as soon as there is a tendency for white bloom to develop.

Rinse under the tap and follow this by a rinse with distilled water. Stand on edge and allow to dry. Do not touch the surface with anything until dry. When dry, put a small quantity of dry rouge on a very soft cloth or a clean piece of chamois leather and polish the coating very gently.

On no account must the waste silver solution be kept, as it oxidizes to an explosive substance.

At the time of writing the cost of aluminizing a 6 in mirror works out at around £20. The cost of the above chemicals presently works out at about £16. Bearing in mind the difference in time the coatings last, it must be said that silvering has fast become the more expensive and is possibly mainly of interest from an experimental or historical point of view.

Care of the mirror's surface
There are, of course, steps which should be taken to ensure that the mirror coating lasts, whether it is aluminium or silver. Neither type will stand continual exposure, so some sort of covers must be made for those periods when the telescope is not in use. A very soft material should be kept in con-

tact with the surface and a good idea is to cut a piece of hardboard to a circle just a little larger than the mirror. Stuck on to the face of this could be a circle of foam rubber or sponge, to the front surface of which has been fastened either a piece of soft cloth, or better still a circle of chamois leather. The softness of the sponge will then allow the leather to follow the curve of the mirror with only a very light pressure. Small tabs of either string or elastic band can be used to hold the cover lightly in place. The cover can be improved by the addition of a collar which will slip snugly over the cell holding the mirror.

Never rotate the cover once in contact with the mirror surface, only press it into contact. Though the surface of the cover may be soft, bits of dust or grit will doubtless find their way on to the mirror during use and these will scratch if dragged over the mirror surface. When taking the cover off the mirror for viewing, always it take indoors. Any damp that the cover may have absorbed will then be dried out ready for its replacement after an observing session. Do not let it get too warm though, since this might cause another problem. During observing the mirror will get pretty cold and to place a warm cover over it could cause the mirror to dew up, it will then remain damp while under the cover and this will degrade the coating.

After a prolonged observing session the mirror may well become dewed up anyway. This happens when the temperature of the glass drops below that of the surrounding night air which causes condensation to form on the mirror. Again if the cover is replaced when the mirror is in this state the damp under the cover will remain to damage the coating. This will only happen on very still nights. A slight breeze or light wind will keep the mirror dry. The unfortunate thing is that the very still nights are best for observing, so dewing becomes a real problem. One good idea is to blow the mirror dry with a hair dryer on a cool setting.

One further aid is to place cling film over the end of the telescope tube, if it is of the closed type. There are some who have been lucky enough to find a piece of film optically good enough to leave in place while viewing, using it as a sort of optical window. It is certainly worth a try, though I must confess I have never found a piece as good as this. It is certainly worth doing for those periods when not in use. There are some who actually place cling film over the mirror between use, though this is a little dangerous. The mirror could well get scratched if great care is not taken, while if any damp is trapped beneath it will not dry and the coating will suffer.

The diagonal should also be protected with a cover. Ideally use a piece of PVC tube, a little larger than the diagonal holder, so that it fits snugly over it. Inside, a piece of elliptically cut card covered with sponge and chamois leather should be placed to lie at the same 45° angle as the flat, so that it presses lightly into contact with the mirror surface. This also can be held in place with string or rubber bands. Be careful though, if it is not held securely the occasion might arise where it could fall down the tube on to an uncovered mirror and this would do no good at all.

There are further steps which can be taken to lengthen the life of an aluminium coating, though these are applicable to aluminium and not silver. The mirrors must not be held in place in their cells by any other metal than aluminium. If other metals are used, moisture could bring about staining by electrolysis.

If after a long period of use the mirror becomes so covered with dust as to affect its efficiency, do not attempt to wipe this off. The mirror will certainly be scratched if this is done. The time has probably come to remove and wash it. To do this the mirror should be immersed into a bowl of lukewarm water to which a small amount of pure soap powder, such as Dreft, has been added. With the surface of the mirror just a couple of inches below the water's surface, make a piece of cotton wool into a ball about 3 in (76 mm) across and carefully pull this across the mirror in every direction. No pressure should be applied, the weight of the waterlogged ball will be sufficient. Continue this for about 30 seconds, remove the mirror, rinse under the tap and stand it on its edge on either a piece of absorbent cloth or blotting paper. If properly clean the water should run away as if the surface were greasy. If the water clings in certain places then those areas are still not clean, and a further attempt at washing should be made. After rinsing under the tap and standing on end, very carefully dab away any water droplets with a soft cloth or tissue—dab, do not wipe.

An aluminium-coated mirror may be so washed perhaps eight times during the coating's lifetime. It should never be washed immediately after the application of a fresh coat. If it is found to have finger marks on it when the new coating is examined, then the mirror can be washed after about two weeks. If left, the marks will eat into the surface eventually.

Chapter 15

Mounting the optics

The primary mirror cell

There are many functions that the mirror cell must perform. It must be strong, yet not so massive as to affect the ability of the mirror to reach thermal equilibrium. It must hold the mirror securely, not allowing unwanted movement, yet not causing any strain on the glass component it is holding, whatever the angle the telescope is set to. It must provide uniform support for all parts of the mirror while being fully adjustable in every way so that easy alignment of the optics is allowed. Finally, removal of the cell from the telescope should be simple for those times when cleaning or recoating is required.

From reading the above it might seem rather difficult, but all of these requirements can quite easily be met in a simply constructed cell with no precision workmanship needed, though obviously the larger the mirror the more involved things become. For a mirror of 6 in (152 mm) diameter the problems remain small. Even a plate glass mirror can have sufficient thickness for flexure of the glass to be minimal. This will help with the problem of support.

Depending on the diameter of the mirror and the ratio of its thickness, this problem of support does change. Generally for mirrors of up to 8 in (203 mm) a three-point support is sufficient. The positions of those points is important since the idea is for each support to carry an equal weight. Any inequality will result in sagging of the mirror and changes in the form of the mirror surface.

The three-point system is the most simple. Here the points themselves should be positioned on a circle the radius of which is $^7/_{10}$ the radius of the primary itself, and spaced at intervals 120° apart. For mirrors over 8 in (203 mm) and up to 24 in (609 mm) diameter, nine-point, or even eighteen-point, support systems become necessary. Each of these is still based on the original three points, the nine points being obtained by balancing three circles or triangles on the original points, each of these again having three points of contact with the mirror.

The eighteen-point system becomes a little more involved but the best known of these, the 'Hindle' design, is still quite simple, with no precision engineering needed. Here we introduce three bars which are again balanced on three original support points. These in turn have two further balance points at each end, making six in all. On these points triangles are balanced which themselves have three points of contact with the mirror giving eighteen in all. Naturally the positioning of the points must be correct as shown in Figure 56.

For a 6 in (152 mm) telescope you can adopt the three-point system. For the actual construction of your cell a visit to the local scrapyard should solve the main problem. What you need is a cell shaped rather like a shallow cake tin. A steel brake drum from an old car is just what's needed, having an inside diameter of around 7 in (177 mm) to match that of the tube. Cut a circle of plywood the same size as the mirror. Countersink three holes in the upper surface of the wood in the positions already described and stick a ball-bearing in each to form the actual support points on which the mirror will rest. Another possibility is to cut three 1 in (25 mm) squares of plastic bubble pack and glue these down into the same positions. Even a complete 6 in (152 mm) disc of bubble pack will work, giving good support all over the mirror.

If the reason for a three-point support system confuses you, think of a stool with three legs and one with four legs. The one having three, 120° apart, will always sit firmly on level ground. The four-legged stool will often rock, having only three of the legs contacting the ground at any one time. Packing will be needed under the fourth to make it firm. So by adding a further support, such precision would be required that it becomes impractical.

The adjustment of the cell must now be considered. This can easily be done in one of two ways. Either the plywood disc can be made to change its angle slightly within the cell or the whole cell can be made to adjust at the end of the telescope tube. Whichever method is used this adjustment should again be based on three points 120° apart.

If the former is preferred start by marking a circle centrally on the plywood with a radius half that of the main mirror. Mark off three points at 120° intervals to fall midway between the points of support for the mirror. Drill holes

Figure 56. Positions of the supports of various mirror cell flotation systems; (a) three point, (b) nine point, (c) eighteen point (Hindle).

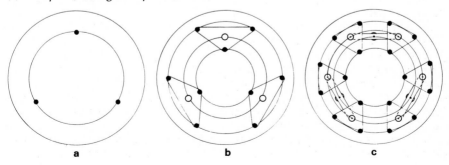

a   b   c

through the plywood disc to align with three similar holes through the back of the metal cell. Insert bolts through each of the holes which should be countersunk slightly into the plywood face, so as not to protrude to spoil the support of the mirror. Push the bolts through the plywood and place three small springs on each with washers at each end. Push the bolts through the back of the cell trapping the springs between the wood and cell base. Hold the whole thing in position from behind with wing nuts. These will be the means of adjustment. When screwed tightly enough to compress the springs it will be seen by tightening or loosening the wing nuts, the plywood disc will vary its angle within the cell. In this way fine adjustment can be achieved. The main problem here is that if the wing nuts are accidentally knocked, alignment is spoiled. Re-alignment is so easy that it is not a considerable problem, however, if preferred, ordinary nuts, with lock nuts, could be used on each bolt. The cell can then be secured to the tube with small bolts. If it does not fit the tube exactly, lugs can be made which fix to both tube and cell.

The second method is to allow adjustment at the points of fixture to the tube. This is perhaps the more difficult, but can be done by fixing three L-shaped pieces of steel, brass or aluminium to the tube at 120° intervals around its bottom end. If your cell has a wide flange then drill three holes in this to match the positions of the pieces of angle. If there is no flange fix another three pieces of angle to the cell, again to match up with those on the tube. Slot a bolt through each, again trapping a spring between them and tighten up. Adjustment will now be possible; by the further addition of

Figure 57. The method for attaching mirror cell to tube, allowing adjustment of the whole cell with the mirror in a fixed position.

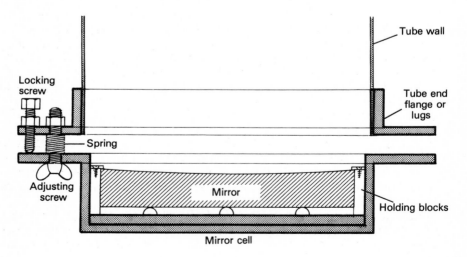

Figure 58. Fixture of mirror cell to tube using springs for cell adjustment as with Figure 57 but with separate extra adjustment of the mirror cell within the tube attachment.

three locking screws to each piece of angle and to one side of each spring, the aligned position of the cell can be held, cutting down the number of times re-alignment is necessary.

All that remains now is to arrange a way of holding the mirror gently but firmly in the cell. For this at least three pieces of aluminium strip, bent in such a way to allow fixing to the underside of the plywood disc, are needed. They should be long enough to run up the side of the mirror having a small lip at the top to stop the mirror from falling out of the cell. None of the strips should actually be in contact with the mirror, but close to it. The thickness of the aluminium strips should be around $^3/_{32}$ in (2.5 mm) and $^3/_8$ in (9 mm) wide. If pieces of chamois leather are glued to the inside face of these, filling the narrow gap between them and the mirror and made to follow the lip at the upper end, all areas in contact with the mirror will be soft but sufficient to hold it in position. In this way no strain will be imparted on the glass (see Figure 59). We now have a cell which meets all the basic requirements, though obviously the design would only be suitable for mirrors up to 8 in (203 mm) diameter.

Brake drums vary in size from around 6 in (152 mm) to 24 in (609 mm) so you can see the range of telescope size for which these can be used. Unfortunately, the larger ones tend to be a little on the massive side, so, if used,

Figure 59. Simple mirror cell for a 4 in (10 cm) reflector showing the ball bearings for the three-point support. Also shown are three metal strips which hold the mirror in place and one of the three springs used to aid adjustment.

thermal problems will arise. Alternatives need to be found in these cases. It is a good idea to have a band of aluminium rolled to whatever diameter is required. By fixing a thick plywood base to this and a ribbed structure made from thick aluminium strips, a lighter but strong cell is obtained. The whole thing can even be encased in glass fibre. This will improve strength still further without adding greatly to the weight, and thermal problems will be minimal. I was involved in the construction of such a glass fibre cell for an 18 in (456 mm) reflector and it proved very successful indeed.

   As with every aspect of the engineering side of telescope construction, great possibilities will be found from whatever environment you live or work in. For instance, my work used to be in the printing industry, where machines were run by belts from pulley wheels fixed to motor driven shafts. The pulleys came in all sizes and when some were removed for scrap or replacement it became a habit to beg them from the firm, realizing their potential as parts for a large telescope. Now the mirror cell of my 16½ in (419 mm) reflector is made from two such pulleys, the larger one forming the portion holding the cell with the mirror and fixing the system to the tube. The hub has been removed and a steel disc welded in its place. The steel ring of the cell containing the mirror is from a smaller 18 in pulley wheel with the hub and spokes removed completely, and a full diameter steel plate welded in position as a base. Added to this is a ¾ in (18 mm) thick plywood disc for strength.

The mirror itself is held in the cell by six hardwood plugs. A small piece of aluminium is fixed to the top of each and these just overlap the mirror top to stop it falling out. The plugs are held in position by grub screws through the steel ring. These are not tightened on the mirror, they insert into holes in the wood to ensure the mirror is in no danger of moving. Each of the plugs is faced with chamois leather. All major parts of this cell were scrap, only the minor parts being made specially. So you can see what can be done for a minimal cost.

Anyone contemplating the building of a telescope would be well advised to pay one or two visits to local scrapyards. It is amazing what is to be found. Once your mind is geared to telescope building, you will see that the yards are filled with potential telescope parts. Mind you, even I could never have envisaged what happened to one group of enthusiasts who, on paying a visit to their local scrapyard, were lucky enough to come across an 8 in Celestron Cassegrain Maksutov telescope! Apparently it had originally belonged to a member of a very well-known pop group and had been dumped when the owner had no further need for it. After some attention it was restored to working order, and now forms a major part of the enthusiasts' observatory equipment.

There are obviously many ways to construct a mirror cell. Ideas given here are only meant as a guide. There is plenty of room for imagination.

Diagonal mounts

The secondary mirror of the Newtonian must not only be mounted in a way to support the glass properly, it must also be suspended in the centre of the telescope tube without causing too much of an obstruction. This causes problems of its own but though seeming at first rather difficult, they can be overcome in a relatively simple way.

As with the main mirror, the diagonal mirror must be held without any undue strain on the glass. Diagonals are pretty small, especially for the size of telescope we are considering. Their relative thickness means that the support system need not be complex. It must, however, be fully adjustable to allow alignment of the optical train of the telescope, and of course it must be accurately angled to deflect the beam as required. Usually the diagonal is supported by three or four vanes which is why the support is often referred to as a spider mount. It may even be supported by a rod passing across the tube or a single strut from the tube, sticking out into its centre.

If the three-vaned spider mount is employed then the vanes should be positioned at intervals of 120° as shown in Figure 60(a). A good rigid structure is obtainable if brass or aluminium strips are used and fixed edge on to the optical axis. In this way the vanes can have considerable width, in the order of 1 in (25 mm) or more, yet they can be thin enough so that when end on they cause only minor light loss.

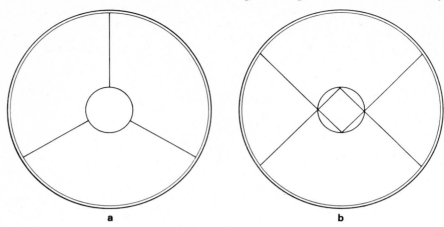

Figure 60. The arrangement of (a) a three-vane and (b) a four-vane spider mount.

If a four-vaned spider is chosen, the same metal strips can be used but their arrangement should be as seen in Figure 60(b). This will give a much more stable fixture. If they meet radially, vibration could be difficult to avoid. The vanes should be bent at right angles at each of the ends and screwed or bolted to the telescope tube and diagonal arrangement.

The actual diagonal holder itself could either be made of brass or aluminium tube, cut off at an angle of 45° at one end, then plugged with hardwood at the other. PVC tubing will also suffice being cheaper and easier to work with, wall thickness is greater however, with more of an obstruction resulting. If the diagonal is to fit snugly into its tube, the position of the inner face of the hardwood plug should be such that it stops the diagonal from entering the tube completely. The mirror surface should protrude just a small amount from the angled end. The space formed beneath the diagonal itself can be filled with cotton wool for packing. The mirror is then held in place by two or three small strips of aluminium, each bent over at the very end to form tiny lips, which just reach in beyond the extreme outer edge of the diagonal. These are then fastened to the holder with screws. In this way the glass will not be pinched, nor will it fall out of the holder. There are some who suggest sticking the diagonal to the holder with double-sided sellotape, but this could be disastrous should the secondary become unstuck during use. Damage to it and the main mirror could occur should it fall down the tube.

The details given above for the diagonal holder would be fine for telescopes of the 6 in (152 mm) to 8 in (203 mm) range. With larger primary diameters and shorter f ratios, the diagonals become quite large, needing better support. In such cases an ellipse of plywood can be fixed to the angled end of the holder. The upper surface of this should have a number of pads cut from

Figure 61. Cross-sections of various diagonal holders and their methods of adjustment; (a) uses three screws which push against the holder making it rock on a rounded nut inside the holder itself, (b) also uses three screws but employs springs between two plates to allow adjustment and (c) has six screws holding, and allowing adjustment to, a central shaft.

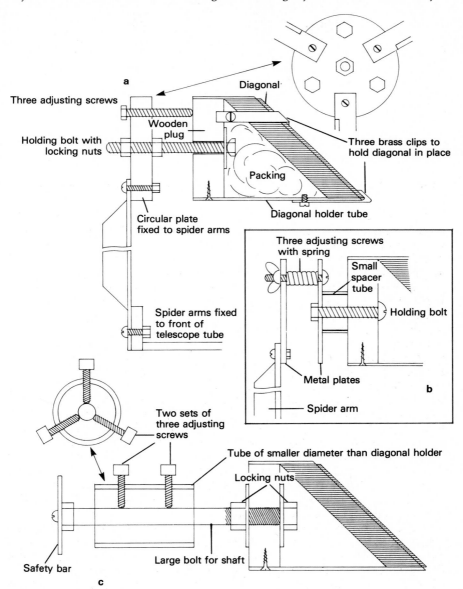

felt, leather or carpet, glued to it, on which the secondary can rest. A full-sized piece of plastic bubble pack might again be useful here. The mirror can then be held in position as before.

The adjustment to allow alignment can be dealt with in several ways. Most simple is to insert a threaded shaft, or long bolt, through a hole in the centre of the holder's hardwood plug. On the portion of the bolt inside the holder a nut, which has had one face filed to form a dome, should have this face brought into contact with the plug. If it is wished the plug can be protected by a washer at this point. The holder is then held in position by three bolts, the ends of which are brought into contact with the outside face of the wooden plug. These three bolts are themselves threaded through a collar situated a short distance from the back of the holder. They should be spaced at intervals of 120°, each having a locking nut. By tightening or slackening these bolts in turn the holder will then be seen to rock on the domed nut, giving the adjustment required. This, together with a certain amount of movement up and down the shaft, in order to bring it into line with the eyepiece aperture, affords the full range of adjustment (see Figure 61(a)).

Another possibility is to have a fairly thick shaft inserted through the hardwood plug and held in a fixed position by locking nuts. The shaft then passes through a piece of tubing held at the centre of the spider vanes. Two

Figure 62. A diagonal mount using springs, as shown in Figure 77(b), to aid adjustment. This is achieved by tightening and slackening the wing nuts. Note that the spider vanes are made from narrow angle aluminium with portions of one side of the angle cut away.

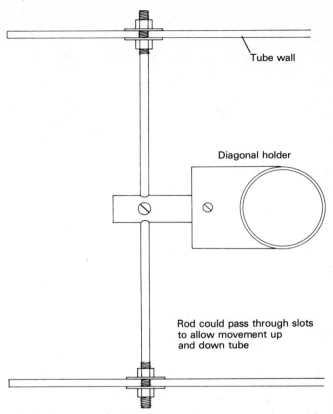

Tube wall

Diagonal holder

Rod could pass through slots
to allow movement up
and down tube

Figure 63. The principle of a full-diameter, single-bar diagonal mount.

sets of three holes are then drilled in the tube at 120° intervals, each set separated by 1½ in-2 in (37-50 mm) and then threaded. Grub screws are then inserted to hold this shaft central in the tube, which needs to have a greater inside diameter than the shaft's thickness. These screws will allow adjustment in all directions. There is one vital safety precaution which must be taken if this method is used. Some form of stop must be fixed to the upper end of the shaft to stop the whole arrangement sliding through the screws should you ever forget to tighten them properly.

Even more simple diagonal mounts are possible. Perhaps the better of these which still retains some degree of adjustment is a single bar stretching across the centre of the tube, situated at right angles to the eyepiece position. This bar is then made to pass through a hole drilled in the centre of a short piece of shaft protruding from the centre of the hardwood plug. This can be tightened on to the shaft by a simple grub screw, or by cutting a slot

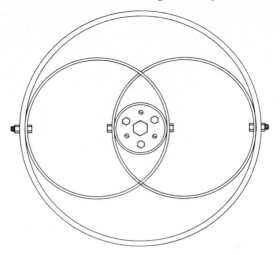

Figure 64. The arrangement of a ring spider mount of the type used to do away with the diffraction spike effect resulting from other types of spider arrangements.

from the end of the shaft down to the hole. In this case the shaft can then be squeezed to tighten on the bar by inserting a small bolt through the end of the shaft and tightening with a nut. With this, movement of the diagonal up and down the shaft together with rotation around it is given. To give a small added movement up and down the optical axis, short slots cut in the tube at the points where the shaft is fixed will solve the problem.

Because of the type of obstruction the spider mount creates, diffraction spikes are formed on star and to some extent planetary images. This is disliked, especially by photographers. There is a way of reducing the effect by the use of two rings or a curved single bar for the spider support. It is quite effective but does complicate things. If photography is your scene it could be worthy of consideration, but visually the diffraction effect is not really too objectionable and need not cause concern, especially if you prefer to keep matters simple. See Figure 64 for the structure of the ringed spider mount.

For those who decide to use a prism instead of an elliptical flat as their secondary, perhaps the best idea involves the structure having vanes meeting at a central tube with screw adjustments already described. A different holder will of course be necessary at the end of the shaft to carry the prism itself. This need only be a piece of aluminium angle cut to the same width as the prism, made to hold it securely by bending the ends of the angle over slightly.

An even simpler way is to have two corner brackets. Bend one arm of each so that they stand vertically when the other is placed flat. Bolt the two flat arms to the tube wall so that the vertical arms are spaced a distance apart which is slightly greater than the prism width. Use a strip of aluminium for the prism holder as before. When bending to a right angle make a sort of loop at the apex of the angle. This can be done by shaping around a thin bolt. Pass a similar thin bolt through this loop when the prism is in place, and through holes drilled in the vertical arms of the brackets. Tighten slightly with a nut. This will hold the prism and its mount in place allowing some adjustment by rotating it slightly on loosening the nut. No strain will be imparted on the glass. The arms will clamp to the aluminium holder if this is cut slightly wider than the prism itself. With this arrangement alignment to the eyepiece aperture can be obtained by brute force. Just bend the vertical arms until they are in the correct position. Crude it may be, but it does work.

Eyepiece mounts

This is an area in which it is possible to either buy an eyepiece mount or make one for yourself. Whilst it has to be admitted that the prices of ready-made eyepiece mounts are high there are some good ones. Considering what you get for your money they can be excellent value. There are also some bad ones around so take care.

Figure 65. A simple secondary prism mount. This has been purposefully placed out of alignment—it is brought into line with the eyepiece aperture simply by bending the main support arms. Although crude, it is very effective. Further adjustment is by swivelling the prism on the holding bolt and by sliding the whole arrangement back and forth in slots cut in the telescope tube.

The precision with which the quality eyepieces are made, plus their adaptability can only be matched by those who have access to a lathe and are reasonably experienced in its use. The same applies to the fittings which can also be purchased, enabling eyepieces of different diameters to be fitted. Until recently only three types have been available. Most popular are the rack and pinion mounts. With these a focusing wheel is used to rack the eye-piece in and out. This enables fine focusing even with fairly high magnification. They are certainly worth going for, though occasionally they may seize or tighten up making it difficult to focus. Other less convenient, though still effective, types have a threaded eyepiece tube to allow fine focusing or, more simply, a push fit tube, where to achieve focus the tube is just slid in and out. Though the least convenient of all, the latter is quite useful for low powers. There is a danger of the eyepiece sliding through into the main tube with this type. All types are purchasable, the latter being the cheapest.

Even though some expertise is required to make mounts as good as the better manufactured ones, it is still possible to come up with excellent alternatives. One fine source of beautiful brass rack and pinion mounts are old magic lanterns. Unfortunately these can now be very difficult to come by, in these days when anything older than twenty odd years is jealously guarded

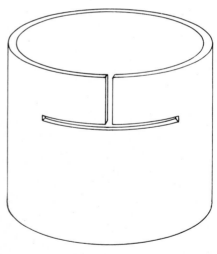

Left *Figure 66. Beautiful rack mounts made of brass, such as this one, can be obtained from magic lanterns.*

Below left *Figure 67. By cutting a piece of tube in the way shown it can be made to accept eyepieces which are slightly too large or too small. This is not an accurate method but will suffice if a lathe is not available or machine-made mounts are considered too expensive.*

Right *Figure 68. An eyepiece mount with helical focusing. Part of a damaged government surplus telescope was used for this.*

for its antique value. If you find one you are likely to be charged as though it were made of solid gold. You could be lucky, however, so keep an eye open. The focusing for my 16½ in (419 mm) is such an item. So valuable is it to me, that as I have progressed from one telescope to another, the rack mount has moved with me.

The push-fit type of eyepiece is the easiest to make and this simply requires a thick-walled piece of tube fastened to the telescope, in which a smaller diameter tube fits snugly—this holds the eyepiece itself. It is not always easy to find tubes which fit perfectly. A neat little trick, though far from precise, is to make two little saw cuts into the top of the thicker tube: one lengthwise from the upper end about ¾ in (19 mm) long and another at right angles to this for about ½ in (12 mm) either side of the first cut and at its bottom end (see Figure 67). This will allow the tube end to be splayed out or closed in just a little making for a light but flexible fit.

Most reasonable eyepieces are made to fit a drawtube of 1¼ in (32 mm) inside diameter, so this would be the best size to go for. It will be possible to adapt eyepieces of 1 in (25 mm) outside diameter but 2 in (50 mm) outside diameter would be a problem. Since the latter are less common it is something we can live with. Some older eyepieces have a threaded 1¼ in (32 mm) barrel. Adaptors can be made for these but a lathe would be needed.

A further novel idea and one which works well is to have a spiral slot cut in the outside tube and a screw with a deep round head fixed into the inner tube. If this is made to ride in the slot then, by rotating the inner tube clockwise or anticlockwise, it will move in and out. It is like a portion of a large thread. If greased lightly or rubbed with candle wax the movement can be quite smooth. It is sometimes possible to cannibalize old government surplus telescopes, which are otherwise damaged, in order to find such pre-made parts, which will often be of brass and do the job nicely (see Figure 68).

There is one innovative eyepiece design which solves most problems. This brilliant simple idea was originally thought up by John Wall, a member of Crayford Manor Astronomical Society. He has called his design the Crayford Eyepiece Mount. It is so simple that anyone with moderate ability can make one. In fact they have even been constructed with meccano.

The principle of the Crayford is for the eyepiece tube to be carried by two pairs of wheels, each pair forming a V. The angle of the V is such that the wheels rotate in the direction of the tube movement. This tube is then held firmly in position by a rotating shaft on the opposite side. To this shaft are fixed two more wheels used for focusing. As this shaft is rotated fine move-

Figure 69. Diagram showing the principal parts of the Crayford eyepiece mount.

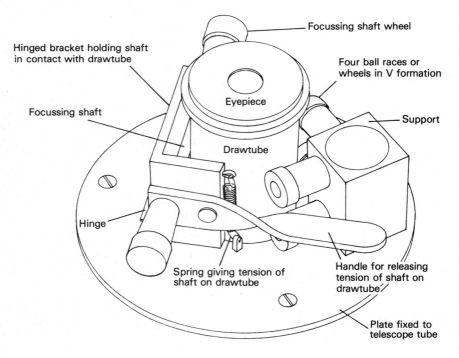

Figure 70. The Crayford eyepiece mount based on the original design by John Wall.

Figure 71. A simple Crayford made from Meccano parts.

ment is achieved. Pressure of the bar on the tube is afforded by a strong spring. If the shaft is fixed through a piece of aluminium channel and attached to the eyepiece face plate by a hinge, then by lifting the whole thing away the tube can be removed.

Ideally each eyepiece should have its own tube to make changing easy. An addition of a flange or collar to the upper end of each will stop the tube either slipping or being wound through into the telescope tube. Slipping can occur if the spring tension is not sufficient, or if a heavy eyepiece is used or camera attached. This can be prevented by the addition of a pad of felt on the inside of the channel support for the focusing shaft, making contact with the shaft and acting as a brake. Rather than go into detail of how this can be made, a glance at Figures 69, 70 and 71 will give a clearer idea. You will see there are many possibilities for slight modifications.

On the point of the eyepiece face plate, there is not really a great deal to be said other than that it might be advisable to make this adjustable for about 1 in (25 mm) up or down the tube. This gives extra adjustment for the optical train particularly in cases where spider adjustment is limited. For round tubes matters are made much easier if the plate is made in the manner shown by Figure 72.

Figure 72. Eyepiece plate made by bending a sheet of brass so as to give a flat surface to a round tube on which to fix the eyepiece focusing mount itself.

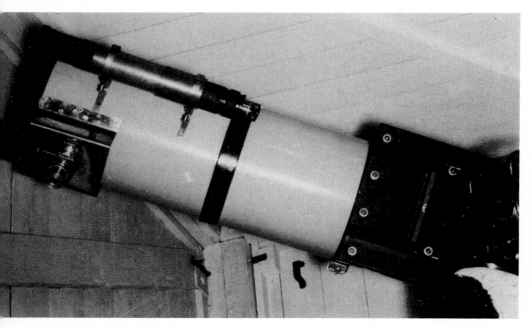

Chapter 16

Telescope tubes

The function of the tube is to hold all of the optical parts and their respective mounts in alignment so that the optical train can be accurately maintained. By fixing this tube to a mount the telescope can be directed to all parts of the sky without upsetting this alignment. There are more varieties of tube design than there are telescope types, ranging from the obvious closed cylinder type to various frame or lattice designs, right down to single planks of wood or even tubeless telescopes. Each have their advantages or disadvantages as usual, though they are all effective, relatively easy to construct and cheap. To give you an idea of what is possible I will work through the most common of them one by one.

Closed tube

The main problem with this type is that air currents within the tube often affect definition. This can be slight or considerable, depending on the materials used.

The closed tube can be either in the shape of a cylinder made of glass fibre, PVC or steel, or it could be multi-sided, octagonal or square and made of wood. The cylindrical shape is usually preferred simply because it is aesthetically pleasing and actually looks like people imagine a telescope should do. Yet it can lead to difficulties. Attaching fixtures to a rounded surface is far more difficult than if the surface were a flat one.

The purchase of round glass fibre tubes, through telescope dealers, is possible, but can prove expensive. They can be home-made by anyone who has a mind to, but it is not easy and in any case the mould needed would probably do just as well. There are points in favour of this material, however; its thermal properties are such that tube currents are kept to a minimum, the rough interior when coated with matt black is perfect for cutting down on spurious internal reflection and it also has the benefit of being strong but very lightweight.

PVC tube is ideal. It comes in all sizes and is easy to work with. It is pretty rigid while still being lightweight. Thermal properties are again quite good and tube currents are not too objectionable. It is also pretty cheap and so common that occasionally it can be acquired for little or nothing.

Steel tube can be made of sheet metal with steel bands for strength, though these days it is often not worth the cost. Another way to come by such tubing is to find scrap air ducting. This is usually galvanized which is an advantage since it is resistant to rust. The problem is that it is not too easy to deal with—drilling holes, cutting, etc can be difficult. Also the material can become pretty cold during the night and tube currents can be considerable. It is, however, very rigid. If you are able to work with steel then fixtures can be bolted to it securely. With any closed tube, always ensure it is 1-2 in (25-50 mm) larger in diameter than your mirror, allowing even more with larger telescopes.

For the fixing of attachments, octagonal or even square tubes can be more suitable. If made of wood, fixtures can be very easily screwed into place. The shape of these also makes mounting easier, since with round tubes circular bands usually have to be made to hold the tube to the mounts and this can be costly. For a 6 in (152 mm) instrument, a square wooden tube would certainly be easy, quick and cheap to make. The main objection to wood is that after a while it may warp. If this is not too drastic, adjustment of the mirror mounts will be enough to account for it.

If a square wooden tube is decided upon, make this from four pieces of ⅝ in (16 mm) plywood each 8½ (216 mm) by 48 in (1.2 m) long. Fasten these together with screws in the manner shown in Figure 73 with four plastic corner brackets at each end. These are found in most DIY stores. Extra strength and better performance will be afforded if three or four squares of plywood, each with a 6¼ in (158 mm) hole cut with a jigsaw, are glued to three of the sides and spaced at intervals along the tube. In this way one side

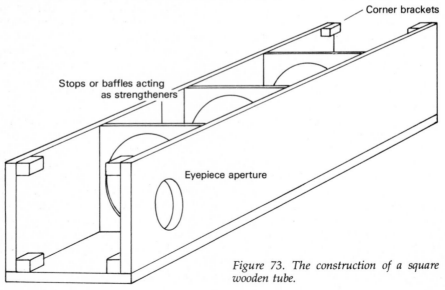

Corner brackets

Stops or baffles acting
as strengtheners

Eyepiece aperture

Figure 73. The construction of a square wooden tube.

will always remain removable so that access to the interior is always easily obtained.

If a door is made at the mirror end forming a sort of flap, the mirror cell can be fastened to this flap, again for ease of access. When this flap is closed it must be secured well to stop unwanted movement when the optics have been aligned. The simple way to deal with this is to drill a couple of holes through one side of the tube into the flap and use pegs to stop any such movement.

Wood is quite good for countering tube currents. As a further aid to this open sections in the skin of the tube should be incorporated, simply by leaving a few sections of the panels open or even one whole side if preferred. Openings of this type keep air flowing through the tube freely, improving definition. All closed tubes should at least have a door toward the bottom end, large enough to get the cover through to the mirror. If the tube is completely closed ventilation is helped by leaving this open when viewing.

Open frame tubes

Though these do not suffer from tube currents in the way that closed tubes do, they suffer in other ways. Most problematical is stray artificial light which can fall directly on to the optical parts, reducing contrast. Also dewing is more likely when the optics are exposed. There is a way to get round the problems, this is to have closed sections around the optics.

Their construction can be of narrow tubing, such as electrical conduit for smaller instruments or even scaffolding or steam piping for larger instruments. If the piping is made to pass through various rings at regular spacings along the length of the tube, then a reasonably rigid structure will result. Fixtures can be attached upon various plates bolted to the struts while the ring at the back end can take the mirror cell.

Of all the various designs for open frame tubes, by far the best and most rigid is the Serrurier A-frame type construction. It is a standard structural principle adapted to the manufacture of telescope tubes for both professional and amateur instruments. It is simple to make and may be built with metal angle, any amount of which can be found in scrapyards in whatever size required. My own 16½ (419 mm) reflector was built cheaply in this way, using angle bed framing.

If part of one side of the L-shaped angle is cut away for about 2-3 in (50-75 mm) at the end of each strip, it gives flat surfaces which can be fixed to each other and other parts of the structure. Short, strengthening strips of metal, flat or angled, can be added near the apex of the A shape. The convenience of this A-frame design is the way in which various shapes of the different components can be linked together. For instance, from a good strong central box shape, attaching the tube to the mount, the A sections can join easily to the mirror cell and spider/eyepiece end, which themselves can be square, octagonal or circular. (See Figure 74.)

The rigidity of the structure is amazing. If it is felt that steel angle is too

Left *Figure 74. One of the strongest open tube designs, the Serrurier A frame, used here for the author's own 16½ in (42 cm) reflector. It is simple and exceptionally rigid—in fact it is the design used for the Palomar 200 in (500 cm) Hale reflector. In this case the tube struts are made from angled bed framing—note how the various shaped sections are easily joined together.*

Right *Figure 75. A telescope using a single plank instead of a tube. It is simple and effective for telescopes up to about 6 in (15 cm). It is ideal as a basic telescope for testing out optics on the stars prior to fixing them into a more permanent structure. The diagram also shows a very simple equatorial mount described later.*

heavy for smaller telescopes, narrow aluminium angle can be used to great effect, this being easily obtainable quite cheaply from most hardware stores.

Single plank structure

It may be difficult to believe that telescope structures of this type can be constructed and be effective, but the single plank type is most successful, beautifully simple to make and amazingly inexpensive. The basic problem is the same as with any open design, this being stray light and dewing of the optics, however, if used in dark sites the major problem of the two is solved.

The design is simply to have one long plank somewhat longer than the focal length of the primary mirror. If this plank tapers slightly, to be narrower at the eyepiece end, the balance point will be nearer the bottom, so the telescope will be more convenient to use when mounted because the eyepiece will be higher and more accessible.

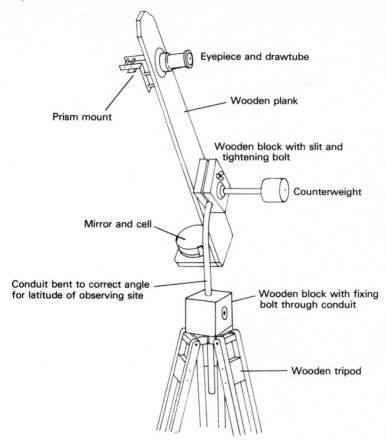

Eyepiece and drawtube

Prism mount

Wooden plank

Wooden block with slit and tightening bolt

Counterweight

Mirror and cell

Conduit bent to correct angle for latitude of observing site

Wooden block with fixing bolt through conduit

Wooden tripod

At the bottom end of the plank a further square piece of wood with sides equal to the width of the bottom portion of the plank is fixed at right angles to it. This is the base to which the mirror cell is to be fixed. At the upper end drill a hole for the eyepiece aperture at a position that should be worked out as given earlier. On the mirror side of the plank, a mount for a prism secondary, of the second type described at the end of the last chapter, should be fixed. Since this plank design is suitable mainly for instruments of 6 in (152 mm) or smaller it may be that a prism secondary arrangement of this type is quite suitable. The eyepiece mount on the outside face of the plank can be of any type desired, but should be of light construction.

Finally the inside areas of all tubes, be they open or closed, should always be painted matt black as should any fixtures inside such as the spider mount, diagonal holder and the inside of the eyepiece mount, this will cut down or eliminate stray light.

Chapter 17

Mounting the telescope

I have already described the various common types of mountings there are. The time has now come to make a choice. Whatever type you decide on, the most important thing is to go for a sturdy construction giving extreme steadiness. No matter how good the optics are, if the mount is spindly and shaky their value will be greatly impaired. Even poor optics can be put to reasonable use if the telescope is fixed to an adequate mount. There are many who advocate the fact that the heavier a mount, the better, but weight does not always mean strength. Lightweight constructions can be surprisingly strong if made properly.

For a 6 in (152 mm), most mount designs will prove useful, even the altazimuth. Obviously in most cases it is better to go for an equatorial of one type or another, but for simplicity and sturdiness the altazimuth is not to be despised. It is a very usable mount despite the obvious guidance problems, and even these can to some extent be overcome. The mount could be made cheaply.

Home-made altazimuth

An altazimuth mount of a size required to hold a 6 in (152 mm) telescope can be made from metal or wood and can of course be portable. A very novel idea is shown in Figure 76. In this case the majority of the structure has been made from 1 in (25 mm) scrap electrical conduit, even the tube. By glancing at the photograph it is possible to appreciate the simplicity but effectiveness of the design.

The stand is a fixed tripod, approximately 2 ft 6 in (76 cm) high though this of course can be variable. The instrument shown is a 6 in f10. Shorter f ratio instruments having a shorter tube will require a higher stand for ease of viewing. Fixed to the top of the stand is the flywheel of an old Mini. At the centre of this is fixed a ballrace, through which a 1½ (37 mm) steel shaft is passed and centred by a brass bush fastened to a fixed shelf further down the tripod. A collar at the top of the shaft stops it falling too far through. This is the movement in azimuth. Actually the half shaft of an old car would do very nicely here and many of these are to be found in large numbers in car breakers' yards, costing only a few pence.

At the very top of the shaft is fixed an A-shaped plate which is then attached, at the wide end, by strong hinges to a similar plate forming part of the tube. This gives the movement in altitude. It will not retain a fixed position for viewing without further modification, however. This is achieved by means of a bar attached to the tube by a movable joint. The bar in turn passes through two nylon cleats fixed to the tripod top. By means of a bolt to which a handle is fixed, the cleats will be made to tighten or slacken off the rod. By slackening off, the rod can be moved up or down through the cleats and then clamped in the desired position.

Continual adjustment of the rod is of course necessary in order to keep up with the changing altitude of any object under view. By having a break in the upper part of the rod, fine adjustment in altitude will be possible with the introduction of a short threaded bar. One way that this can be achieved is to have each half of this bar threaded in opposing directions with a wheel fixed at the half-way point. If the two halves are each made to screw into threaded holes in each section of the rod, then, by turning the wheel one way the rod sections will be brought together, while turning it the other way will move them apart. This will impart a fine up and down movement to the telescope tube (see Figure 77).

Further hand-driven slow motion, this time in azimuth, can be achieved by the fixing of a small bar through the stand top A plate, the lower end of which should carry a small cog to engage the teeth of the flywheel. By turning this shaft, the fixture of a handle will help here, the telescope can be

Figure 76. A home-made 6 in (15 cm) f10 reflector on an altazimuth mount.

Left *Figure 77. The threaded section of the altitude adjustment rod. By rotating this section fine movement in altitude is afforded. It comprises a knurled nut and fine screw thread.*

Right *Figures 78 and 79. Two further altazimuth mounts, both made largely of wood. The mount shown in Figure 79 uses a half shaft from an old car for its azimuth motion.*

moved fractionally in azimuth. With practice, careful adjustment on both axes will allow successful tracking of celestial objects.

Most of the structure shown in the example given here is welded. For anyone not in a position to do this, normal bolt fixing will do just as well. This will allow the dismantling of the whole thing. There are naturally many adaptations of this design as can be seen from Figures 78 and 79. The basic design is the same in all cases but the stand and mounts can, if desired, be made largely of wood. In Figure 79 a vehicle half shaft has been used to give azimuth movement.

The Dobsonian

Perhaps one of the best and most simple telescope mount designs to appear in recent times is what is known as the Dobsonian. The design is of the altazimuth type again, but has become popular recently because it is so cheap and simple to make. It can be adapted to small or large telescopes. Perhaps the most appealing thing about it is that it has brought the large aperture instrument within the range of the average amateur. Most

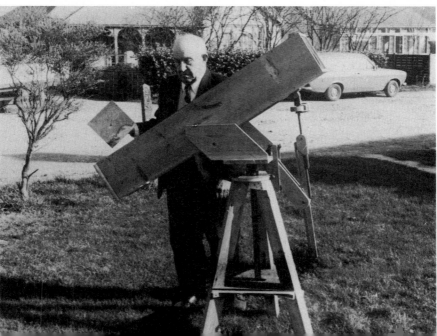

surprising is that it has been possible by use of this design to make telescopes up to 30 in (76 cm) which are still portable! The whole thing can be made of everyday materials and despite its simplicity can be made to look very attractive.

The telescope tube itself has a large box-shaped section which holds the mirror. This can be made of blockboard for smaller types, though thick marine plywood is advisable for larger aperture instruments. The back panel of the box can be made into a door or flap allowing access to the mirror as described earlier with the square wooden tube. Many Dobsonians have their mirror mounted on a piece of carpet, though I find bubble pack better. Other mirror supports may be preferred however. Protruding from this box is the upper tube section. In many examples large cardboard tubes are used and protected with a lacquer coating. Usually these are obtained from carpet manufacturers, though in this country such tubes are not easily come by. However, there is absolutely no reason why this upper section should not be of the frame type with a square or octagonal section at the top to hold the secondary and eyepiece mounts. In this case less weight is involved in the upper part which will be of advantage as is to be seen presently. The whole tube is then made to sit in a box-shaped base (see Figure 80) the back side of which should be open, with the front side short to allow unobstructed tilting of the telescope tube.

Figure 80. The base section of the Dobsonian, one of the most simple and effective altazimuth designs. The whole structure can be built largely from wood and made to look very attractive.

Right *A larger dome than that shown on page 100, which the author helped to construct. It is made of angle iron covered with hardboard panels and finished with a coat of aluminium paint.*

Below *An octagonal observatory housing an 8½ in (21.5 cm) reflector on a German equatorial mount. The hatches, window and door are open for viewing.*

Two unguided photographs to illustrate what can be achieved with only a camera and tripod. **Left** *The constellation of Orion. A 15 second unguided exposure on ASA 400 slide film. The original shows the star colours clearly as well as showing more stars than are visible to the unaided eye. The vivid red colour of the gaseous nebula M42 in Orion's sword, resulting from the Hα emission, is also clearly visible. A standard 50 mm lens was used.* **Below** *The brilliant planet Venus close to the planet Mars in February 1985 made a fine sight at the end of twilight. A few foreground trees add to the scene captured with a 15 second exposure using a standard 50 mm lens and 400 ASA slide film.*

Right *Prime focus image of the Moon taken with a 16½ in (42 cm) reflector at f5.3. The 1/125 second exposure makes this little more than a snapshot with no drive necessary.*

Below *Total eclipse of the Sun on 30 June 1973. Taken from on board MS Monte Umbe off the west coast of Africa with the 4 in (10 cm) reflector described in the text using 1/125 second exposure at f8 prime focus on high speed Ektachrome, 160 ASA processed to 320 ASA. There is a slight loss of sharpness due to vibration from the ship's engines.*

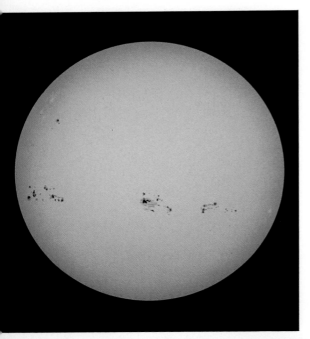

Left *An observation of sunspots near maximum activity made by projection on 18 October 1981. 12.35 UT. 3 in (76 mm) OG.*

Below *The Orion Nebula (M42). A hand guided exposure of 20 minutes with a 135 mm telephoto lens plus a ×2 converter (f7) and high speed Ektachrome was used, showing what can be achieved with the minimum of equipment.*

Figure 81. The lower tube section of the Dobsonian. The edges of the circular pieces are covered with formica and fit into the 'U'-shaped cut-outs of the base section, riding smoothly on small teflon pads.

Movement in altitude is obtained by two disc-shaped pieces of wood attached one each side of the tube box section, positioned at the centre of balance. The discs are then made to sit into two semicircular cut-outs from the centre of the upper edge of the long side pieces of the base box, which have the addition of three to five teflon pads glued down at spaces around this cut-out. The tube side discs then rotate in these and movement will be made very smooth by covering the edges with a strip of formica or similar material. If balanced properly this easy movement will stop at any position required without tendency to slip.

This still leaves the azimuth movement to deal with. For this the whole box-mount section is made to sit on a base plate, which has a circular or octagonal piece of formica-covered plywood or blockboard. Even veneered chipboard will suffice for lightweight small instruments. Sticking up from the centre of this should be a centering pin. A hole drilled through the centre of the box-mount base will fit on to this centering pin. By the addition of several teflon pads to the underside of the mount box, an easy sliding rotation will be obtained over the base board, again with no slipping when stopped.

The main parts of the construction, excluding optics, can be finished in a weekend if in the 6-8 in (152-203 mm) range. The telescope is light, totally portable and can be taken by car to any observing site, being re-assembled in only a few minutes. It can form either the major instrument of a home observatory or can be an ideal portable extension.

Equatorials

It is the type of movement afforded by the equatorial mount that makes it generally more desirable than the altazimuth mount. Therefore any equatorial, even if of simple construction, is preferable. Tracking the heavenly bodies across the sky is easier but it is not so easy to achieve the stability of the altazimuth without some care.

Possibly one of the most simple mounts of this type that I have ever come across is shown in Figure 75. Obviously stability in this case leaves a lot to be desired, but it works quite well and is cheap. It is really only suited to smaller reflectors of around 4 in (102 mm).

The principle is to have a large square wooden block cut from a piece of 4 × 4 in (102 × 102 mm) hardwood. This should be fastened to a stand such as a tripod or fixed pedestal. A 1 in (25 mm) diameter hole drilled down through its centre can then take a piece of electrical conduit. This can be held firmly in position by a coachbolt passing through both the block and conduit itself. A foot or so of the conduit should be allowed to stick above the block, and bent about half way up to an angle equivalent to the latitude of the observing site. The angled part of this now becomes the polar axis. By aligning this with the pole star, the telescope to be fixed on the shaft will follow the stars reasonably well.

To mount the telescope on the conduit another block of wood should first be fixed to the telescope tube at the centre of balance. A flat-sided tube is best suited for this, particularly one of a simple plank construction. Drill a hole through this block to allow it to fit on to the upper end of the conduit. A thick saw cut is then made into this block, parallel to the tube side and half way into it to encounter the full length of the hole. The coachbolt that fastens the tube to this block, passing right through it, should have a couple of washers placed between the tube and block, with a wing nut on the portion protruding from the block side opposite the tube. By tightening this wing nut, two things will then happen. The declination movement of the tube will be made less free, while the saw cut will be squeezed together thus tightening the block on to the conduit. This will stiffen the right ascension motion. The whole thing can then be slackened for moving quickly around the sky from object to object but tightened to hold it firmly in place at fixed positions. Finally fix a bar to the side of the wooden block opposite the telescope. Weights added to this will then act as a counterbalance to the telescope.

It must be admitted that this is a crude sort of equatorial mount, though with slight modification it could be scaled up to take larger instruments. Even if this is not to be your permanent instrument it is a way to test your optics to see how well they perform. Also, you have the benefit of a temporary telescope to use while building something more substantial, which is far better than having unused optics lying around.

The equatorial mount most frequently encountered by amateurs is the German design. It is the type most commonly used by telescope manufacturers for amateur-sized instruments. In fact it is possible to purchase well-made mounts on their own, building the rest of the telescope around it yourself.

Constructing such a mount is not difficult, successful efforts being achieved in ingenious ways. One simple method is to start with a piece of strong steel pipe, such as heavy duty steam piping which can then either be sunk into a concrete base, or, even better, held in place by bolts, the heads of which have themselves been sunk into a concrete base. The top of the pedestal must then be sawn off at the required angle for the polar axis followed by the fixing of a plate. Either this or a complete head will be needed to take the equatorial mount. Whichever, it is necessary to have a firm angled platform, preferably with provision for slight adjustment to allow polar alignment. Obviously there are other alternatives for the pedestal. I know of amateurs who have used sections of old telegraph pole or just plain brick pillars. In the latter case a reinforced concrete head can be moulded to take the equatorial mount, it is cheap and very solid. If the brick is felt too unsightly it can easily be covered with some sort of cladding.

For the polar axis, all that is required is a steel shaft carried between two plumber block bearings. Such bearings are immensely useful to the telescope builder. Many may be found in excellent condition complete with housing in the local scrapyard. They may seem dirty when found but when stripped down the inner parts are usually in perfect condition, protected by liberal amounts of grease.

Fastened to the upper part of the polar shaft must be a flange, to which is bolted a rectangular plate centrally placed and at right angles to the polar shaft itself. This plate carries the declination axis which can again be a simple steel shaft carried between two more of the famous plumber block bearings. Once more the whole thing will be found to be too free moving, so some form of restraint will be required. Sections of brake shoe, made so that they tighten down on to the various shafts, will suffice.

The cradle to hold the telescope tube is fixed to a further flange at the end of the declination shaft. When the telescope is mounted in this cradle the whole arrangement will be hopelessly off balance, so therefore it will need to be counterbalanced with weights at the opposite end of the declination shaft. The heavier these weights are the better, since this will bring them closer into the mount. Inadequate weights will require to be located at the end of a long shaft. This will add to the clumsiness and instability of the arrangement.

The weights themselves are not difficult to obtain. Weightlifters' bar-bells are ideal, especially if these can be second-hand, otherwise they tend to be a little expensive because their weight is measured exactly. An alternative is to obtain some large empty paint tins and fill these with cement or concrete. Before pouring the cement into the tin, position a piece of wooden dowel of

the same diameter as the declination shaft, centrally in the tin, and covered with wax paper. When the cement has dried, the dowel is removed leaving a hole through the centre of the weight. A circular hole is then cut into the base of the tin. If it is wished to replace the lid for the sake of appearance, then a central hole must also be cut into this. The whole weight can then be slid on to the shaft and held in place by small collars. When painted the weight will look quite neat. It may be that more than one will be required but they are so easy to make that this will not be a problem.

Years ago lead was found in abundance in many scrap or demolition yards at relatively little cost. It was then possible actually to melt the lead inside empty paint cans, inserting a piece of shaft through the centre while still molten. Small very heavy weights were then possible. With the present value of lead this is a less likely possibility though for anyone who has some old lead pipe lying around, it is worth remembering.

A rather novel German equatorial construction built by my father involved the use of an anti-aircraft identification telescope of the type originally used by two observers during World War 2. This had all the requirements for adaptation to an equatorial mount. It was purchased at a reasonable price because all of the optics had been removed. It had slow

Left *Figure 82. An 8½ in (22 cm) reflector on a German equatorial mount adapted from a World War 2 anti-aircraft identification telescope.*

Right *Figure 83. Close-up of the mount shown in Figure 82. A short piece of steel shaft serves as the polar axis and rides between two plumber block bearings.*

motion movement in both right ascension and declination as an added luxury, together with calibrated scales in both altitude and azimuth. Originally the instrument was used as an altazimuth but by tilting it to the correct angle it became equatorial. Very little modification was required.

The polar axis was made by separating the double sighting instrument from its base and rejoining them with a steel shaft which was carried by two plumber block bearings mounted on a brick and moulded cement pedestal. Accuracy of the bolt positions in the moulded cement head was first acquired by the construction of a wooden frame. Once the bolts were found to have the correct position in the wooden frame, the whole thing was encased in cement. Further adjustment to align the polar axis was possible even though the fixing bolts were no longer movable. Either of the plumber block bearings could be packed up with washers of varying thickness to alter the polar axis angle. Further to this the plumber block bearings have slots not holes through which the bolts fit. This allows for a certain amount of swing in the polar axis. The cradle which held the telescope tube was fixed by a collar to the end of one of the sighting arms, while the counter-balance weight was fixed on a shaft protruding from the other.

Government surplus material such as this is fast becoming very scarce. It

Far left *Figure 84. An easily-constructed wooden fork mount for a small reflector.*

Below left *Figure 85. The base of the wooden mount uses a piece of wood to give the required polar axis angle. Different lengths of wood will give different angles to the polar axis, making the telescope usable as an equatorial at different latitudes.*

Left *Figure 86. The cradle holding the telescope tube fixed to two large bolts riding in ball races in the upper portion of each fork arm. The free movement of the polar axis is slowed by tightening the bracket at the lower end of the polar axis.*

is therefore much more expensive these days than it used to be. The idea does show, however, just what is possible with a little imagination and thought. People often say to me 'But I have no engineering skill at all'. My father was an artist, he never even learned to drive a car and his engineering skill was nil. His inspiration in telescope building was born simply out of the desire to view the heavens through a well-made telescope of his own construction.

One of the major criticisms of the German equatorial is that it can be a little unstable. Also it prescribes a larger circle of movement than a fork-mounted instrument of similar dimensions. For those who therefore prefer the fork mount there are several simple ways of building these. The example given here uses wood for most of its parts.

The base of the mount is a wooden platform which, if desired, can be fixed to three short legs for steadiness. Fixed to this base is a second wooden platform fastened at one end to the base by hinges. This platform carries the polar axis shaft, once more situated between two plumber block bearings. The angle of this platform can then be altered to suit the latitude of the observing site, and fixed by a piece of 3 in × 2 in (76 mm × 50 mm) wood, cut to the length required. This gives a solid angled base. Originally the idea was designed to be used to observe the total eclipse of the Sun in 1973, just off the west coast of Africa. By inserting a shorter piece of wood to give a lower angle to the polar axis it was possible to make the instrument equatorial for the latitude 19° N required. Then by replacing it with the original piece of wood the instrument was reverted back to an equatorial for the 53° N latitude of the original observing site. Simple but effective.

The upper end of the polar axis shaft carries a flange which instead of carrying a declination axis shaft, is now fixed to the base of a fork made to carry the tube.

The fork itself may be made of wood carefully jointed and bolted to make it rigid. Or it could be made of channelled aluminium. Toward the upper end of each fork arm should be fixed ball races, or plumber block bearings at the very top. These are to hold the declination shafts fixed to the telescope tube. In the example given the tube is held in a cradle. This would not be necessary if the tube were square. Once again free movement of the arrangement needs some restraint. This can be done in the form of a clamp on the polar axis or even by a slow motion drive to be discussed later.

Because of its stability and compactness, the fork is ideal for larger amateur telescopes. My own 16½ in (419 mm) shown in Figures 74 and 87 relied almost entirely on acquisitions from the scrap pile. It has a substantial base made of heavy angle, bolted and welded together, though bolts alone would suffice. To give weight to the base, yet at the same time allow the provision of relatively easy removal, a concrete paving slab is placed across the bottom, on which a large number of house bricks are stacked without being cemented together. With large permanent pier telescopes you should always build them in such a way that, if you move house or have to resite the telescope within your own grounds for one reason or another, it can be moved without difficulty or loss of observing time. It would not be a happy state of affairs if on moving home a large part of your telescope had to be left behind because of immobility. I imagine the new owner of the property would be none too pleased on finding a great structure in his garden either, possibly having no idea what it might be other than perhaps some sort of giant sundial. The loose bricks, apart from being useful as ballast, also perform another function, originally unforeseen. They efficiently reduce vibration. The bricks themselves do not look very pretty so simple cladding of the base with plywood gives a much more pleasing appearance. This is only decoration and in no way improves the function of the instrument.

Incorporated on the base structure you will need three platforms. There should be one each side of the upper end, made of steel plate and bolted or welded in place. These each carry a shaft between two plumber block bearings on which a large steel roller is fixed. Running between these rollers is a large diameter steel wheel such as a pulley wheel or machine flywheel. Fixed in the middle of this wheel, and running down to a third platform attached to the bottom of the mount base, is a steel shaft. This in turn is held in a larger plumber block bearing fixed to the third platform. This steel shaft is the main polar axis. Adjustment for polar alignment can be achieved by packing up any of the bearings to alter the angle of the polar axis or by swinging the whole base slightly, which is free standing and not too heavy prior to packing with bricks.

Since the large wheel is to form the base of the fork arms holding the telescope, there is a danger of the whole thing being top heavy. The large bearing at the bottom of the polar axis will stop the whole thing tipping up. Ideally the polar axis shaft needs to be weighted, to take some if not all of the strain off this main bearing. This is achieved by constructing a large cone and filling it with concrete. In my case the cone was an adaptor used in an air ducting system to reduce down from a large diameter ducting to one of smaller diameter. If this cone were filled completely with concrete then the problem of removal would crop up. By sectioning off the cone into four parts with wooden partitioning, then filling each section with concrete, it is possible to remove these if need be. This was done before the galvanized ducting was fixed which is again for looks only.

The fork arms are made from iron girder, though they could be made of

Figure 87. A fork mount for a 16½ in (42 cm) reflector. The forks are made of steel girder obtained from a demolition yard and the base is filled with loose house bricks. Because of the way it is constructed the instrument can be resited in one day, despite the fact that it weighs over a ton.

channel aluminium for smaller instruments. In this case the arms were bolted and welded together for added strength. Bolting alone would be sufficient if the bolts used were strong enough. At the top of each fork arm is a plumber block bearing. These are for the declination axis and carry the shafts attached to sides of the telescope central box section. The beauty of these bearings is that they are to some extent self aligning. To ensure proper alignment, however, place a shaft from one to the other and through each, then bolt the bottom half of the housing into position.

To restrain the declination movement, a large fine-toothed cog fitted to one of the declination shafts, and held with a clamping screw, is made to run in a worm gear fixed to the fork arm. A wheel or flexible drive cable will give slow declination movement but by releasing the clamping screw the original free movement returns.

Movement in right ascension is a different matter, ideally this should have a synchronous motor drive. In this case there are two possible points for the fixture of this drive, a normal 24 hour drive on the polar axis shaft or a drive on an extension to one of the roller shafts carrying the flywheel. Obviously there is already a reduction to be accounted for in the movement required here, which will have to be worked out. This will depend on the size of the rollers and flywheel used. In the latter case a less powerful motor will be needed since it is in effect in lower gear.

The mount just described and illustrated is obviously for a large telescope, it can of course be scaled down making a very solid mount for any size of reflector.

Alignment of the equatorial mount

Before leaving the subject of mountings, there is one further consideration. For an equatorial to keep track on the stars for prolonged periods it must be set up correctly, to the meridian and at the correct angle.

To find the meridian, use an astronomical almanac to find out what time on a given night the Pole Star is at its upper culmination, or in other words directly above the polar point. Direct the telescope so that the star is exactly in the centre of the field of view. The telescope is then in the plane of the meridian. Bring the polar axis into alignment with the tube. This is done by moving the polar axis then relocating the star, until an accurate alignment is obtained. It may not be possible to get it exactly right in just one night, but get it as close as possible.

The polar axis will still need to be set to the same angle as the latitude of the observing site. This can be checked by using a low power magnification and positioning the Pole Star in the field of view once more. The star is not situated on the true pole but about 1° from it. So, if the field of view is close to 2°, when positioned exactly south in the field at the time of its upper culmination, the star, if allowed to drift, should prescribe a circle around the edge of the telescope field round a point exactly in the centre of the field. If this is so the tube is aligned at the correct angle. If the polar axis is so angled that it is parallel to the tube, it too will be correctly aligned. This can now be checked by rotating the whole mount. The star will then be seen to prescribe its path quickly instead of waiting for diurnal motion to carry it around. Since the latter would take 24 hours the whole path would not be observable in one session anyway.

If the mount is a fork type, point the telescope to the pole and spin the mount checking at certain points to see that the Pole Star is moving around the edge of the field. If of the cross axis or German equatorial type, move the mount through half of one rotation, wait for 12 hours and repeat. This method is not possible with an English mount unless it is of a horseshoe type.

Further checking of the alignment can now be carried out by locating another star, perhaps one situated close to the celestial equator. Follow the star for a while to see if it remains central in the field. If not, further adjustment will be needed. If the star is seen gradually to drift south in the field the polar axis is pointing to the east of the meridian. If it drifts north, the axis is set slightly to the west. This only applies to the stars. The Moon is not an ideal choice for testing alignment because it moves independently against the star background. This movement is quite rapid, becoming noticeable after only a few minutes.

If a permanent pier mount is to be used for the telescope, then the base will need to be roughly aligned when at the initial building stage, so that only minor adjustment will be necessary when the instrument is complete. It is presumed that such an instrument will need a substantial concrete base continued some way below ground level. It should be aligned roughly north-south and have a good flat level top which must be checked with a spirit level before putting the final layer of cement on the base. A good idea is to set a number of half house bricks, flat end up in the concrete, checking them against each other with a beam spirit level. When satisfied that they are all correctly level allow to dry, checking at odd intervals. Then apply the final layer up to the top of the bricks, scraping along the top, finally, with a wooden plank.

Preferably while the cement is still wet, though starting to dry, find out what time the Sun actually transits that day, again from an astronomical almanac. At this exact time, hold a plumb line to the south of the base so that the shadow of the line, cast by the Sun, falls centrally across the cement. Then by laying a straight edge along this shadow a line can be scribed into the cement. If it is not possible to do this when wet just scratch a line into the surface—the Sun rarely shines when required. The line will be a permanent guide to the meridian. The mount structure should be built as close to alignment with this as possible, ensuring the necessity for only minor adjustment later.

A simple tripod
If those mounts so far described are too adventurous because all you have is

a pair of binoculars, there is still an advantage in finding some suitable way of mounting these.

Camera tripods which are quite sturdy, and also able to be packed away easily are easily purchased nowadays. They are, however, expensive and are not very high, making for uncomfortable observing positions. There is a way to make your own easily, and with little cost, which will probably last for years. The materials required are as follows:

Six strips of 1 in × 1 in (25 mm × 25 mm) hardwood 5 ft (1.5 m) long
One piece of 3 in × 1 in (76 mm × 25 mm) hardwood 3 ft (91 cm) long
Three ¼ in (6 mm) diameter coachbolts 6 in (152 mm) long plus nuts and six washers
Three 2 in (50 mm) flat L-shaped corner brackets
Six 1½ in (38 mm) long screws or three ¼ in (6 mm) diameter 2½ in (63 mm) long coachbolts.

To begin with take the piece of 3 in × 1 in (76 mm × 25 mm) wood. Cut off six pieces 2½ in (63 mm) wide, and three pieces 1½ in (38 mm) wide. Then take the six 5 ft long strips of 1 in by 1 in to make three pairs. Fasten each pair together with two of the 2½ in (63 mm) pieces as spacers. These should be situated 9¼ in (241 mm) and 2 ft 3½ in (698 mm) from the ends which will become the tops of each tripod leg. Screw through the long strips into the spacers to fix them into place, then pinch what will be the bottom end of each pair together fixing with the 1½ in (38 mm) screws or 2½ in (63 mm) bolts. The small 1½ in (38 mm) pieces of wood should then be fitted into the

Below left *Figure 88. The upper part of a wooden tripod showing the arrangement of the three sections holding the legs and forming the top platform.*

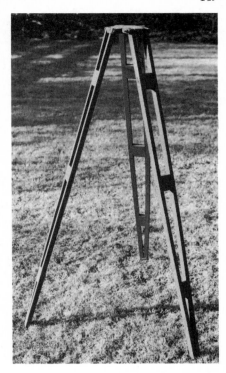

Right *Figure 89. The finished tripod.*

narrowing portion of the legs. It will be necessary to taper these slightly to allow a snug fit. Screw these into place for added strength.

Take the piece of 3 in × 1 in (76 mm × 25 mm) wood which should now be about 16½ in (419 mm) long. Cut three 5¼ in (133 mm) long pieces from this discarding the small piece which was to allow for any discrepancy during sawing and is now waste. These three pieces should now be cut into a particular shape to make the upper platform. They will also hold the tops of the tripod legs in place. As can be seen from Figure 88, the shapes should be such that all three when placed together form a triangular shape.

To do this, find the centre of each piece then, from one edge mark off two 60° angles giving a 120° apex, then saw along these marks. Fix them together into the arrangement shown with three L-shaped corner brackets on the side which is to be the platform's underside. Cut two 1 in (25 mm) square notches into the flat outer edge of each piece for the top of the tripod legs to fit into. Drill right through the length of each piece including the tops of the legs inserting the long coachbolts with washers at each end. Screw on the nuts, not too tightly, allowing the legs to open and close. The upper ends of the leg strips will have to be rounded off so that they swing open without catching.

All that now remains is to drill a hole down through the centre of the platform to take a bolt on which, when fixed into place, can be screwed a small aluminium adjustable camera tripod head. This will take a camera, but it is possible to obtain binocular clamps which will fix to it. If wished extra strength can be given to the platform by fixing a metal plate to it. Finally to stop the tripod legs opening out too far or slipping, fix three lengths of chain to each leg, about two thirds of the way down, taking each to a small central metal ring such as a curtain or key ring. The length of these chains can be judged so that when the legs are opening out a height is given to the upper platform which suits the individual. Shorter versions can of course be made to take cameras or for use by small children.

The poncet platform

The poncet platform is a particularly ingenious rigid mounting of extreme simplicity. It comprises a fixed base board which has a point fixed vertically at the centre of one end, and a piece of wood at the other, cut so that its outward face is angled to match the Earth's equatorial plane. A further platform is then placed upon the base board to pivot on the point while having a wooden attachment on the underside, which comes into contact with the angled piece on the base board, the contacting face of this matching its angle but free to slide over its surface.

It is particularly suited for a standard camera, though guiding periods can only be short. However, with modern high speed films and fast lenses this need not be a cause for concern. Anyway, since the whole thing could be made in an hour or two it is certainly worth attempting despite this shortcoming.

Figure 90. A poncet platform.

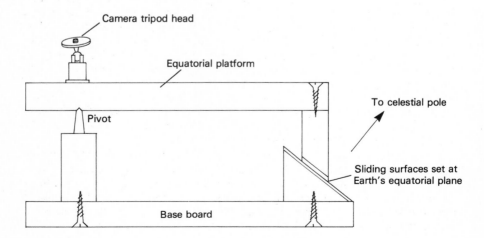

Chapter 18

Collimating a Newtonian

For any telescope to perform properly, correct alignment of the optics must be achieved. The process required for doing this is called 'collimation'. In the case of a Newtonian reflector it is not difficult to do, providing a set procedure is followed.

To help with this it is recommended that you use the following:

Some sort of dummy eyepiece. Simplest of all would be to cut an old cotton reel in half for insertion into the eyepiece drawtube. Better still would be to obtain an old eyepiece, which has been damaged, and remove the lenses. The idea of this is to ensure your eye is always placed in the correct position when aligning the optics, so, within reason, the smaller the eyepiece aperture the better.

A small white paper disc stuck to the centre of the primary mirror. It should have a size just a little smaller than the image of the diagonal holder seen in the primary when viewed through the eyepiece draw tube. It is possible to obtain adhesive paper discs which are easily removable and which will not damage the mirror coating. The centre of the mirror is found simply by cutting a circle of card to the same diameter as the mirror, with a circle of the size required cut out from its centre. Place the large piece over the mirror then place the adhesive disc over the central portion exposed. Although recommended by others I personally feel this latter requirement is less than vital. The eye is well capable of making sufficiently accurate judgement without placing an object of this type on the mirror surface. It is true that the central area of the mirror is not used because it is shielded from light falling on to it by the diagonal and its holder, but I have found problems with the idea when trying to observe an object close to a bright Moon. Light from the Moon illuminates the white disc, spoiling contrast.

To carry out the collimation, point the telescope toward a daylight sky, allowing plenty of light into the telescope. Look through the dummy eyepiece to see the position of the diagonal first of all. By means of the adjustment screws on the diagonal mount, align the flat itself so that it is centrally placed within the end of the eyepiece drawtube, having the reflection of the primary mirror centrally placed within it. To do this, adjustments of the diagonal up or down the tube, toward or away from the eye, perpendicular to the eyepiece tube and finally by rotating the diagonal, will be necessary. Once this has been done, if the diagonal size has been worked out correctly, the image of the mirror should be just a little smaller than the diagonal. Too much smaller, or even too big, will result in light loss.

With the image of the primary central in the diagonal, it will be noted that the reflected image of the diagonal and its spider in the primary will be off centre. This should be centred by means of the adjusting screws of the mirror cell. With small telescopes this may be possible from the observing position. If the telescope is large then an assistant to carry out adjustments, while you assess the quality of alignment, will be helpful.

The final result will be the appearance of a number of concentric circles, diagonal image within primary image within diagonal within drawtube. Further to this the image of the eyepiece drawtube plus the small eye aperture should be centrally placed within the whole lot. If the white disc is used a small black annulus should show around it, which would be the outer edge of the diagonal image. For very short focus reflectors it is suggested that the diagonal be very slightly offset toward the mirror and away from the eye. The image of the primary mirror will appear very slightly displaced toward the open tube end of the diagonal. It must be stressed, however, that this displacement should be slight.

Generally, for low power, alignment as described above will be sufficient. If high powers are to be used, however, it may be advisable to check the alignment on an extrafocal image of a second or third magnitude star, preferably one close to the zenith. Using a low power eyepiece, moved out of focus away from the mirror, examine the image of the star closely. Flaring on one side of the image will be evident. The help of an assistant will be particularly useful here. Adjustments should now be made which make the star image as round as possible. This is done by carefully displacing the brighter part of the image toward the general direction of the flare. If it is done carefully, bit by bit, success will be achieved quite quickly.

Figure 91. Alignment of the optics; (a) incorrect alignment of diagonal and mirror, (b) incorrect alignment of mirror, diagonal correct, (c) correct alignment of all components.

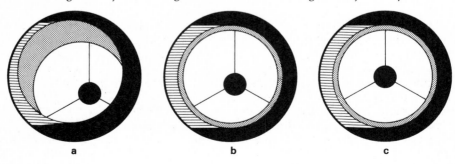

a   b   c

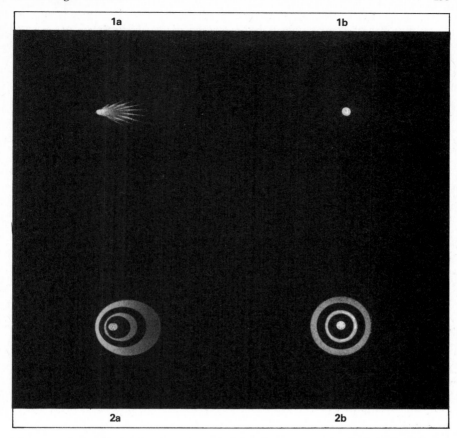

Figure 92. Diagram showing star images with low- and high-power magnification; 1(a) incorrect alignment with low power, 1(b) correct alignment with low power, 2(a) incorrect alignment with high power, 2(b) correct alignment with high power.

Once the image is judged to be perfectly round, replace the low power eyepiece for one giving a high power. Now the diffraction rings will be seen easily. These will be more evident both inside and outside the focus. With the eyepiece once more outside the focus, final, very fine adjustments can be made to centralize the bright star image within the rings. Once this is done, correct collimation will have been achieved.

Obviously with so many adjustments necessary the telescope will not stay perfectly aligned for long. Regular checks can easily be made and any minor adjustments required should be carried out on every possible occasion.

Chapter 19

Telescope fittings and observatory accessories

Up to now what I have outlined is the basic telescope complete with its mount. There are, however, many accessories which can be added to the telescope, irrespective of its type or size. They are not essential to its working capability but they will be valuable aids to its efficiency.

Finders

The moment that a fair degree of magnification is used, the area of sky under study becomes surprisingly small. Even if the telescope has a wide field of view, we are often talking of an area of sky smaller than the apparent diameter of the Moon, and in some cases only a tiny fraction of this. Also faint objects which are selected for study cannot be seen with the unaided eye. Often faint stars surrounding a particular object, which are necessary for pinpointing its position, will themselves be below the naked eye threshold. If we are to avoid the need for lengthy sweeping in the general region, hoping that the object we wish to study will eventually come into view, then the addition of a smaller 'finder' telescope will save much time.

The magnification of such a finder does not need to be high—powers of 5× to 10× being ample. A fair light grasp is of greater value here. Additionally the instrument eyepiece should have cross wires so that accurate sighting on an object can be achieved.

It is often possible to get hold of old ex-government surplus telescopes which make excellent finders though these are all the time becoming scarcer and more expensive. An ideal source of good finders is the local junk shop. Frequently binoculars which are damaged are sold for very little. As binoculars they may be useless, because they have become hopelessly out of line. Split the barrels, however, and you will have one if not two perfectly adequate monoculars useful as finders. Even if there is still a problem with their alignment it is a simple matter to remove the objective and the eyepiece and place them in a new tube, making a splendid finder.

If you are not lucky enough to drop on such an item, then objectives of 1½-2 in (37-50 mm) diameter can be purchased fairly cheaply. If already in a cell, so much the better. A low power eyepiece will also be required, though in this case a fairly cheap one will do. It is, in fact, possible to obtain eyepieces which already have cross wires incorporated, but if not, to add your own is simple. The wires must be in the eyepiece's focal plane. This may be within the eyepiece barrel itself or far enough away to take it into the draw-tube. Once found solder two pieces of finest fuse wire into position at right angles to each other crossing in the middle of the eyepiece field. These will be thick enough to be visible against a dark sky though some prefer finer cross hairs which they illuminate with a very low light, this is a luxury, however, and not really necessary.

To make the finder, all that is needed is a small length of PVC tubing, a little shorter than the objective focal length, with a diameter large enough to take the objective cell. Fix the cell into one end with small screws. A small dewcap large enough to slip over the end of the main tube should now be added to stop damp and stray light falling on to the objective. The top of an old aerosol can is ideal for this purpose when painted matt black on the inside.

In order to cut out glare within the telescope, stops can be fitted. These take the form of three or four rings cut from black card. Each must have an outside diameter slightly smaller than the tube's inside diameter with circular apertures cut into them. The size of the aperture for each will depend on its position in the tube, as they will need to be spaced out along it. To find the size required simply measure the diameter of the converging beam at the positions of the stops. Each ring will need four small tabs at 90° intervals around the outer edge. One tab on each should be glued, then each ring stuck down in line to a piece of black card in their respective positions, previously marked in pencil. The card should be wide enough to wrap around the rings which can now be done after the addition of further amounts of glue to the other tabs. Then slide the cardboard tube you have

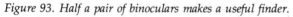

Figure 93. Half a pair of binoculars makes a useful finder.

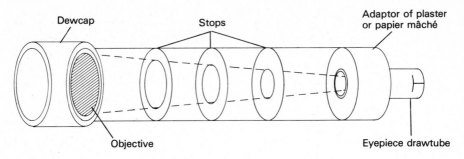

Figure 94. The construction of a finder and positioning of stops.

created into the PVC tube, with the larger aperture ring nearest the objective.

The eyepiece fixture must now be positioned centrally into the other end of the tube. An adaptor can be made from wood, so that the smaller eyepiece tube may be fitted firmly into the larger PVC tube, but if you don't have access to a lathe another method must be found. One way is to take a 1 in (25 mm) length of PVC tube, possibly an offcut from the finder tube. Place the eyepiece tube end down on a piece of board secured temporarily with three or four panel pins around the inside bottom edge. Place the larger offcut tube around this, so that the eyepiece tube is exactly central within it. This can be achieved by first drawing two concentric circles of diameters equal to both tubes on the board with a pair of compasses. The outer tube should also be held in place by panel pins around its outside.

With the whole arrangement now secure, fill the space between the two with plaster of Paris or papier mâché. When dry, remove the outer piece of the tube. If this will not slide off, a saw cut carefully made down its length will enable it to be peeled off. If this adaptor is now inserted into the eyepiece end of the finder tube then held in position by three or four small screws, the finder is complete.

Now there is the problem of mounting the finder on to the main telescope tube. It must be adjustable so that alignment with the optical axis of the main instrument can be maintained. One easy way of doing this is to use circular drainpipe holders, used to fix pipes to the wall. The bases of these can be bolted to the main tube. The finder itself should be positioned in such a place as to be accessible when viewing through the eyepiece, though not so close as to get in the way. With larger instruments, however, more than one finder could be fixed to the tube, different ones to be accessible when set to different positions.

For finder adjustment, three holes should be drilled at 120° intervals around the holder rings and then threaded to take adjusting screws. When

Figure 95. A finder mount made from old drainpipe holders.

Figure 96. A finder mount made from scrap angle iron and rings cut from steel tube.

Figure 97. Finder mounted in an accessible place near the eyepiece of a 16½ in (42 cm) telescope.

Figure 98. Similarly-designed holders for a large instrument to be mounted on the main telescope for use either as a guide telescope or for solar observation.

Figure 99. On a large telescope one finder is often not enough, at certain observing positions it might be difficult to reach. By having a number of finders one will always be accessible.

the finder is inserted through the holder rings, the screws can be finger tightened to clamp it centrally. By adjusting the screws correct alignment will be easily achieved.

There are many other ways in which finders or even guide telescopes can be mounted as seen in Figures 95-98.

Filters

When observing the planets, serious observers often view these objects, not just in white light but in light of different wavelengths. Various coloured filters are used through which the light is made to pass. Interesting effects may then be observed, for instance reddish objects on a planet not seen with a red filter will stand out quite dark with a blue filter. Also red light penetrates deeper into the atmospheric layers of a planet, so by use of different filters it is possible to observe different levels of the planetary atmospheres.

Ideally the light should be made to pass through the filter before entering the eyepiece, the filters being housed in an arrangement which enables easy interchange of the various colours. What is required is a drawtube to fit into the eyepiece mount, taking the eyepiece as normal but intercepted half way down by a mechanism holding an off-centre rotating disc. This disc should have four or five holes each with a piece of different coloured gelatine filter fixed over them. By use of a knob on the front face of the filter disc container, the disc is then rotated to bring the various filters into line with the light rays.

The filter holder could be made of something like a round flat tobacco tin, 4-5 in (102-126 mm) in diameter. If a hole is cut into each side, between the centre and edge of the tin and in alignment with each other, two short sections of drawtube could then be soldered into place. The disc carrying the filters need only be a circle of thin aluminium sheet or stiff card, which has been lacquered to protect it. Fixed centrally to this should be a small cog of the type found in old clocks. It should not be so large as to cover any part of the filter holes. The cog should have a short thin pin through its centre, which is to be held in place by two small central holes in the front and back face of the tin container. If necessary small washers could be glued or soldered in place to strengthen the tin around these holes.

Rotation of the filter disc can be effected in one of two ways. One method is to fix a knob to part of the central pin protruding through the front of the container. This knob can be of the type found on old record players which have screws in them for fixing to a shaft. The other method is slightly better but more involved. Here a small cog needs to be engaged into the larger central cog with a shaft once more protruding through the front face of the container. The knob is then fixed to this shaft. This gives a faster rate of spin to the filter disc, also taking the knob further from the drawtube, thus making it easier to get hold of.

Figure 100. A filter holder.

Figure 101. The halves of the holder are separated here to show the rotating disc and cogs. Four different coloured gelatine filters can be used but one of the holes should be left clear for viewing without a filter.

Solar telescopes

There are those who will wish to make a study of the Sun. Obviously the most important thing to understand is that in no way should the Sun be viewed directly with any optical instrument, no matter how small, unless it is of a highly specialized type. Such specialist equipment is beyond the range of most amateurs. It is possible to view the Sun indirectly and in perfect safety by the projection method, though to do this successfully one or two items of equipment will be needed.

First of all it is not recommended that the main observatory instrument be used if you wish it to be used for other types of observational work. This is particularly relevant if the instrument is of fairly large aperture. The heat concentrated at the eyepiece is very considerable and good eyepieces have literally exploded because of this. Also damage may be caused to the secondary mirror, since heat can become quite intense there also. There have even been cases of wooden tubes catching fire. If the focused image of the Sun has been allowed to fall on to part of the inner tube, while trying to align the image through the eyepiece, this is a considerable danger. It is far better to mount a smaller telescope on the main one in the manner of a finder or guide telescope. Failing this use a smaller, separately-mounted instrument. A 3 in (76 mm) or 4 in (102 mm) reflector would be ideal.

If a refractor is used then some sort of shade should be fitted as seen in

Figure 102. This stops direct sunlight falling on to the surface which is to receive the projected image, allowing for better contrast. To facilitate convenient receipt of this image, so that it can be easily viewed, the fixing of a screen to a bar carried by the telescope tube is necessary. The whole arrangement should be removable if the telescope is likely to be needed for other types of work.

The best way to fix up such an arrangement is to first fasten a bracket or brackets to the telescope tube. These should allow a rod to slide through them to be held firmly in place by fixing screws in the brackets themselves. If the rod is long enough the screen can be taken closer to or further from the eyepiece, thus changing the scale of the projected image.

The screen should have a clean matt white surface. White board would do but this easily damages. A square of formica sprayed with matt white paint would be far better. This in turn can be slotted into a three-sided frame, such as an old metal photo frame with one side removed. If necessary a piece of backing board could be glued to the back of the frame to stop it falling apart. A similar bracket to those used to attach the rod to the telescope can then be used to fix the frame to the end of the rod. Being fixed to the tube in this way means the screen will always be aligned to it, therefore, so long as the telescope is directed to the Sun its image will fall on to the screen. Any sunspots present will clearly show.

If a reflector-type telescope is mounted for solar work a similar screen will

Figure 102. A shade for use when observing the Sun with a refractor.

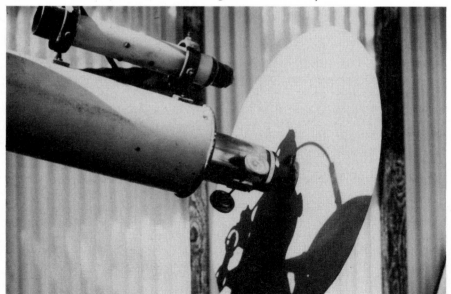

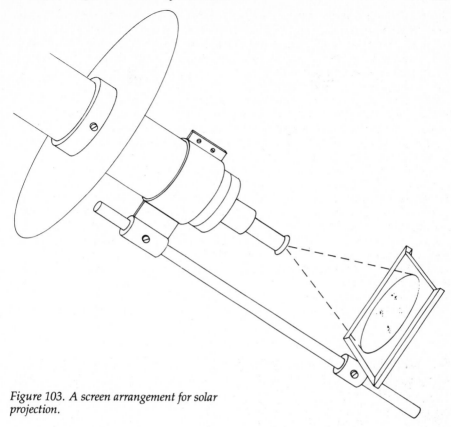

Figure 103. A screen arrangement for solar projection.

need to be aligned to the eyepiece, but the shade used for a refractor will not be needed. Here, to stop direct sunlight falling on to the screen it should be enclosed in a shallow-sided open box. These sides need be no more than 2-3 in (50-76 mm) deep. They will keep a fair amount of stray light off the screen, improving contrast.

The addition of a solar telescope adds greatly to the variety of work that can be carried out in your home observatory, with the added benefit that the Sun is available at a much more sociable hour!

Drives and slow motions
Perhaps one of the most important 'optional' additions that can be made to a telescope which is equatorially mounted, is the provision of slow motion which could be hand or motor driven. The ability of a telescope to follow the stars has already been described with regard to the construction of equatorial mounts. Without a slow motion drive, however, the telescope will

have to be pushed continually bit by bit in a westward direction to keep up with the celestial object in view. While this works all right with small instruments, using low powers and wide-angle eyepieces, the problem of tracking becomes great with large instruments or when high magnifications are employed. Then the addition of a slow motion drive turns from pure luxury to an important observational aid. It becomes vital if long exposure photographs are to be taken through the telescope eyepiece.

The most popular way of fixing up a slow motion is to use a worm and worm wheel. The larger worm wheels are better since they will have a greater number of teeth. The minimum number of teeth a good wheel should have is about one hundred, though if more, so much the better. By fixing the large wheel on to the polar axis shaft and the bracket holding the worm casing to the mount base, the turning of the worm will impart a motion in right ascension. Provisions for disengaging the worm from the wheel will be necessary for fast movement. If the worm wheel is keyed to the shaft, loosening of the grub screws holding the wheel to it will allow the telescope to be slewed around as required.

A hand-driven slow motion is sufficient for most uses except for photography. This is achieved by fixing a wheel for turning the worm, or a flexible drive cable which is useful if the telescope is large and the worm otherwise inaccessible from the eyepiece position. A similar sort of slow motion movement could also be added to the declination axis, though here a smaller worm wheel will suffice. The worm wheel in this case must be fastened to the declination shaft, the worm itself to the shaft casing, or fork arm, depending on requirements. This can also be hand driven in the same way as described for the right ascension drive, however, this is not so important.

For the purpose of photography some sort of motor drive is needed and it is here the problem starts. Clock drives are a possibility, but in most cases these do not have the power to drive anything other than small telescopes. There are also electric motors but the considerations are such that one has to be fairly specialist. Also, I have never been particularly happy about electricity fed to the telescope which, to a large extent, is usually of steel construction. This, plus, the damp conditions usually prevalent during the night, makes for dangerous circumstances. It is therefore my advice to leave the job of fixing up the electric drive to those who know what they are doing. It must be admitted that worm wheels of the type required are generally very expensive, as are electric motors. The problems are complex however, and some of the money saved on building the rest of the telescope is possibly better spent on ensuring that a good drive is obtained.

Setting circles

The addition of setting circles to any telescope can be quite useful. They are also incredibly simple to make, taking the form of two graduated discs. One is to give readings in declination which should be divided off into 360° and fixed on the declination axis. The readings on this should go from 0°-90°-0°-

90°-0°. The other is to give readings in right ascension. This should be fixed to the polar axis and marked off into 24 hours, with each hour divided into five minute intervals, each twenty minute mark being made to stand out more clearly. Readings should go in an anti-clockwise direction.

For anyone who has access to a lathe it will be an easy task to graduate the discs accurately and the circles could be made of brass, plastic or perspex. If no lathe is available, perfectly satisfactory circles can be made of stiff card. The graduations can be marked in pen with the numbers written or applied in dry print. The card can then be protected with lacquer coating or, better still, sandwiched between two discs of perspex; with the edges sealed to prevent damp penetrating through to the card.

To use the circles properly, first the declination circle should be secured to the declination shaft. A pointer, which is to indicate the setting, should then be fixed to the bearing casing or shaft housing. Before final fixing of the declination circle it should be set so that when the telescope is directed to the equator, the reading given is 0°, when directed to the pole it should read 90°. To get this accurately positioned, direct the telescope toward a star of

Figure 104. Two further additions to the telescope are setting circles (only the declination circle is shown here) and counterweights. The weight shown performs several functions; it counters the weight of the guide scope and helps to make the tube bottom heavy to allow the use of shorter fork arms. By making the weight slide up and down a bar any additions to the upper end, such as a heavy camera, can be countered by sliding the weight toward the back end of the bar.

known declination, found previously from a star atlas. Set the circle reading to the pointer and secure to the shaft.

The right ascension circle should also be fixed with the provision for turning or clamping it. Again a pointer should be fixed to the shaft housing on the meridian line pointing to the circle graduations. For setting, note the sidereal time. The circle should then be set to show the same reading at the meridian pointer. Any object of known right ascension and declination can then be found by using the circles.

This is the principle. Frankly I find it a lot of trouble to go to for correct right ascension settings. Many observers prefer to use the declination circle only to locate objects. The problem is the continual need to reset the right ascension circle as time moves on. Unless the circles are dimly lit, the need for the use of a torch, for reading settings, is likely to spoil your eyes' adaption to the dark, making the viewing of faint objects difficult. With practice it will be found to be far easier to locate objects using the star patterns surrounding them.

This does not devalue the usefulness of circles. They really can be helpful as an aid to finding the planets Mercury and Venus during the day, which is the best time to view these. This is done by offsetting from the Sun. By finding the co-ordinates of the Sun and the planet you are looking for, it is possible to work out their difference in position. When this has been done direct the telescope toward the Sun, taking care to leave lens covers on. Alignment can be checked by the Sun's projected image through one of the finders. Then move the telescope the distance required in both axes. Remove the lens covers and, if you have done your sums correctly, the planet should be in the field of view. It does not matter how the circles are set for this to work, only that the graduations are accurate.

Camera mounts

Once a telescope is completed it is not likely to be long before the person using it desires to photograph the celestial objects as seen through it. Whether this be snap shots of the Moon or long exposure photographs of fainter objects, success will be aided by fittings to allow the camera to be held steadily in place. This might be at the eyepiece drawtube itself for photographs through the telescope, or simply a means of attaching the camera to the top of the tube or mount for photographs taken with the camera alone, but having the benefit of the telescope's equatorial movement.

Reasonable pictures of the Moon can be obtained by just holding the camera up to the eyepiece and making exposures of $^1/_{60}$-$^1/_{30}$ of a second, provided a low power eyepiece or just the prime focus is used. However, if the camera is not held perfectly in line with the optical train—which is a practical impossibility—the quality of the photograph will be impaired.

Unfortunately most adaptors require precision threads to allow fixture to the camera body. This should be done by an expert turner, otherwise

Right *Figure 105. Eyepiece tube adaptor screwed to the body of an SLR camera in place of a lens.*

Below *Figure 106. A camera used in place of the eyepiece—the telescope simply becomes an enormous telephoto lens. Prime focus photography or eyepiece projection photography is possible in this way.*

Figure 107. Camera fixed to a telescope with a Barlow attachment for magnified images.

Figure 108. Magnified image of the Moon using a Barlow attachment. Exposures of ½ to 1 second are necessary as the image becomes quite dim with higher magnification. For this reason a drive is needed.

Figure 109. Camera mounted 'piggy-back style' on a telescope, using the telescope's equatorial movement, driven either by hand or by motor, for guided shots of the sky.

damage to the camera body thread might result. Even so the acquisition of such a device should not involve too much cost. All that is required is a tube to slot into the eyepiece drawtube having a thread at one end to accept the camera. If wished the provision for including an eyepiece can be made, or for a second tube containing a Barlow lens which slides in and out of the main tube. Such provisions would allow for the photography of a highly magnified image. In this case, because the image will be dim, long exposure times will be necessary so a good drive is essential. If you do not wish to go to such lengths, then the original arrangement can be used for prime focus photography.

The simplest way of using the telescope for photography is to mount the camera 'piggy-back style' on the telescope tube or mount. This may be done by fixing an adjustable camera tripod head to the telescope rigidly. Even if not motor driven, respectable results are possible by hand guiding. In this way long-exposure, wide-angle photography of constellations or large comets, can be carried out with a standard photographic lens. By use of a telephoto lens smaller areas of sky can be photographed, having their own particular value. These days photographic films are very fast indeed, which helps in astro-photography. Also the single-lens-reflex camera is possibly the best thing that has happened for the astro-photographer. When taking

Figure 110. Guided photograph of the Pleiades made with the camera mounted 'piggy-back style' using a telephoto lens. In this case guiding was by hand and though the star images are not perfect they are reasonable considering the 10 minute exposure used.

pictures directly through the eyepiece the field of view is seen in the camera viewfinder, things were not so easy in pre-SLR days!

Cameras

It may at first be difficult to believe that the ordinary camera can be of value to the astronomer as an astronomical instrument in its own right, but even if mounted on a tripod with an ordinary standard lens, photographs can be taken which could be of scientific interest. On several occasions throughout the year we are treated to various meteor showers. These are periods when the Earth passes through the orbital paths of bands of dust or debris, believed to have been left in the wakes of different comets. As the tiny particles enter our atmosphere they burn up, through friction, in a bright streak of incandescence. Such dust particles are entering our atmosphere all the time, but every so often we encounter these concentrated regions. Then the number of meteors increases, with the actual meteor showers appearing to radiate from particular areas of the sky.

This is where the ordinary unassisted camera becomes of value. Mount the camera on a tripod using an ordinary standard lens. Then point it toward a region of sky where it is felt that meteors are likely to be most frequent. By opening the shutter to make an exposure of between 15 and 30 minutes it might be possible to catch a meteor on film. To succeed in this a fairly fast film of ASA 400 or greater should be used. The lens must be set at maximum aperture, preferably no slower than f2. The exposure setting should be T, for time, or B with a shutter release cable capable of holding the shutter open for long periods.

Figure 111. Interesting astronomical photographs can be taken with a minimum of equipment. This unguided photograph was taken with a tripod-mounted camera using a standard 50 mm lens. The exposure time was 20 minutes, during which time the stars have trailed considerably due to the rotation of the Earth. During the exposure a fairly bright Perseid meteor was recorded which shows an interesting brightness surge midway along its trail.

Figure 112. A battery of cameras mounted with a rotating shutter for meteor photography. (J. Mason.)

The photographs obtained will be very interesting. All of the stars will appear as trails, not points. This is due to the amount that the Earth has rotated during the exposure period. If the camera is directed toward the celestial equator, the star trails will be more or less straight. If directed toward the celestial pole, the trails will prescribe circular paths. If by chance a bright meteor dashed through the region of sky being photographed, it would be recorded as a bright streak crossing the star trails.

It is possible to go even further with this. If a battery of cameras could be used with each pointing to a different region of the sky, the chances of success are considerably increased. By placing these cameras in a specially-made wooden mount (see Figure 112), to which has been added a rotating shutter made to spin in front of the cameras, photographs of meteors then obtained will be of great scientific value.

The shutter itself can be made using an electric motor, such as from a fan, with a known rpm. The fan blades are then replaced with a specially-made blade system where the gap and blade widths have been carefully worked out so that combined with the motor speed they interrupt the exposure every $1/30$ of a second. Any meteor which passes through the camera field will then have numerous breaks along its trail having registered on the film only where the gaps between the blades have allowed the light through. It is recommended that each interruption lasts .03 second. If you have worked things out properly you will know for how long each blade intercepts the

Figure 113. An ordinary camera mounted on an astro compass modified to include a time clock for driven exposures. Although not particularly rigid it has been found quite successful on all but the most windy nights.

Figure 114. A standard camera on an ordinary camera tripod to which a time clock has been added, again for driven exposures. Even when only roughly aligned, quite accurate exposures of up to 10 minutes have proved possible. While the astro compass allows more accurate alignment, this arrangement is simpler and more rigid.

light from the meteor. So by counting the number of breaks in the trail, the duration and speed of the meteor can be estimated.

For those who have no telescope on which to mount a camera, yet still wish to obtain guided photographs of the constellations, the construction of a small equatorial mount for cameras only is possible. These are quite lightweight so drives required need not be very powerful. Occasionally it is possible to adapt certain pieces of equipment to make reasonably good equatorial camera mounts. Figure 113 shows the successful adaptation of an astro-compass, which is fully adjustable, and can be set accurately to any latitude. All that needs to be done is to ensure it is levelled properly. This is easily accomplished by use of the spirit levels included in the construction of the instrument.

Next alignment with the meridian is necessary. If a wide aperture standard lens is used, together with a fast film, exposure times of less than 5 minutes will be sufficient. Even 1 minute will give excellent results. However, with the benefit of a guided mount, slower finer grain films can now be put to good use and it may even be possible to get accurate guiding for 10-15 minute periods. With such short exposures and only standard lenses, really accurate alignment of the mount is not necessary. The longer the exposure required the better it will need to be. The astro-compass has the provision for a hand-driven slow motion. If this is to be used then a small finder telescope will need to be added so that accurate tracking can be ensured. With something as light as this, however, it is possible to use a small clockwork motor. Ideally suited is the time switch mechanism of the type used in central heating systems or even road lamps. These are often found in junk yards. They have a 24 hour movement which, although not very accurate, will be good enough for short periods. They are not very powerful but will be sufficient to carry ordinary cameras. It might be possible to use a telephoto lens of up to 135 mm, but problems in guidance may arise, so trial and error is the order of the day.

Obviously not everyone is going to have access to such ready-made pieces of equipment as the astro-compass. Simpler methods are, however, just as effective. One idea is to use a tripod with an adjustable camera mount attached. These can be purchased at a reasonable price from any secondhand camera shop. Next a small wooden platform should be fixed to the clockwork motor. It must be realized that it is the shaft through the centre of the clock which is the polar axis. The tripod head can be tilted to any angle, so if the arrangement is aligned to the meridian, accurate tracking will be possible. All that is required now is to fix a collar to the clock shaft which has a counterweight on one side and a bracket to hold the camera on the other (see Figure 114). The arrangement is not exceptionally rigid but it works perfectly well in all but very high winds.

Note In these days of exceptionally fast film and wide-aperture camera lenses, good pictures can be taken with no guide at all. If a 400 ASA film is used just mount the camera on a normal tripod with the aperture setting full open. Exposures of 15 seconds will be long enough to show at least all the stars visible to the unaided eye, possibly more. There will also be no evidence of trailing, as 15 seconds is the maximum exposure time which will show no trailing with a standard 50 mm lens.

Light for observational recording

Though this is not a telescope fitting it is such a vital piece of observatory equipment that it is worthy of special mention. When using a telescope at night artificial lights can be a real nuisance, yet to record observations it must be possible to see what you are doing. If the light is strong enough to draw or write with, eye adaption to the dark is affected which makes observation, especially of faint objects, very difficult.

One way to have a reasonably strong light, without affecting the eyes badly, is to use a red bulb. This should still not be too bright and needs the addition of a cover over the upper part to stop it shining directly into the eyes. A useful device would be a small clipboard to hold the paper in place, to which a battery-powered light could be attached. If a switch were built in so much the better. The arrangement should not be heavy or cumbersome in case of the need to hold it for prolonged periods.

Further additions to this could be a clip to hold a pen torch, should anything be dropped in the dark, and a pencil attached by a piece of string. Everything vital is then to hand with the need for switching on a main light or bright torch kept to a minimum. Finally a hook fixed to the observatory wall, or even the telescope, will give somewhere to hang the clipboard so it can be easily located in the dark.

Binoculars

These should be included in every home observatory. I have left them to the end of this section because I wish to underline their value and usefulness, which hopefully you will be able to appreciate now you have read of the grander types of telescopes.

Everyone, even if only having a minor interest in astronomy, would find it of great advantage to own a good pair of binoculars. They are often neglected by the beginner in the initial quest for large aperture telescopes. It is the seasoned observer who, later, really appreciates their true value.

Many people ask which is the best kind of telescope to get for a raw beginner. On the face of it a simple question, the answer is not so easy. The truth is that unless you are prepared to make your own telescope, then, to purchase even a relatively small refractor will incur considerable cost. Even then you are not guaranteed satisfaction. Some manufactured instruments, though expensive are intolerably poor. The result is usually that the newcomer to astronomy is put off for ever. A little guidance at the right time could save this and instead of being disappointed, a long lasting hobby could result.

My advice is always to obtain a good pair of binoculars first and get to know the sky with them. Granted their magnification is low but, despite popular belief, magnification is not everything. If you purchase a 2 in (50 mm) refractor at a cost of around £200 the lens is no larger than each of the two lenses of an average pair of binoculars. The amount of light gathered by the lenses is therefore the same. As you know in astronomy it is the light grasp that is most important. Binoculars then are ideal.

Binoculars should be achromatic. The object glasses of the type used in them would usually only be free from colour when the focal ratio is in the order of f10-f15, or 10-15 times the lens diameter. If it is less than f10 it is difficult to correct the lens sufficiently to make it colour free. The result is that refractors, even with small apertures, are rather long, yet binoculars are always quite short, so how is this problem overcome? The answer is simple. Binoculars are built on a folded principle. By using two prisms situated at certain positions in each barrel, between object glasses and oculars, an instrument which would otherwise have a length of 15 in (381 mm) or so is compressed to one with an overall length of 7 in (178 mm).

The other point is that average prismatic binoculars are very complex instruments. There are a great many optical surfaces involved and it is surprising to me that they are so reasonably priced, in my view, when purchasing them, one is really getting value for money.

There are several makes of binocular and when purchasing a pair always test them first. Take them outside the shop and look through them in order to assess their quality. In doing this there are one or two things to look out for. Binoculars should have at least one independent focusing arrangement, on one or other of the eyepieces. Everyone's eyes are different and this extra is a great advantage.

For a test of image quality look at a narrow object, such as a television aerial, against a bright sky. Place this at the centre of the field and then gradually move the binoculars so as to displace the object either side of centre and watch it closely to see if it distorts, becomes bent or shows colour fringeing. It is unlikely that there will be complete freedom from all of these effects unless a good deal is paid, but you must assess if you feel the effects are tolerable given the price you are expected to pay. The best test will be on star images but this will be difficult prior to purchase, although some vendors might allow approval.

If buying second-hand be sure to give them a good tryout. If you find them difficult or uncomfortable to use, the chances are there is some misalignment of the prisms due to them having been dropped or knocked. Unless the price is very low don't bother, if low enough they can always be split into two monoculars and they will probably work well when not used in conjunction with each other. Finally a check should always be made for scratches on the lenses.

When choosing your binoculars you will see various values or figures printed on them, such as 8 × 30 or 7 × 50. Many people will not have the slightest idea what this stands for, and if you ask the salesman the chances are he won't know either. The first number stands for the magnification, the second for the diameter of the objectives in millimetres, so, 7 × 50 binoculars give 7× magnification and have lens diameters of 2 in (50 mm). Some will give figures such as 272 ft at 1,000 yards. This is an attempt to give the field size. For astronomers this is not much use, they need to know the area of sky the binoculars will show measured in degrees. On average, a good pair of 7 × 50s will give a field 9° across, which is eighteen times the diameter of the full Moon, 10 × 50s should give a 6-7° field.

There are of course binoculars of all sizes. You will come across 11 × 80s, even 20 × 80s. Naturally prices increase with an increased objective diameter. 7 × 50s or 10 × 50s can range from £20 to £150. The binoculars with 80 mm lenses will be much more expensive and you can expect to pay £400 or more. Even so, if good quality, they are worth the money.

Binoculars are surprising in just what they show. They will reveal star colours and a phenomenal number of stars not visible to the unaided eye. They will show craters on the Moon, though to see them best, view at times away from full Moon. The satellites of Jupiter are visible with 7 × 50s as are the phases of Venus, though it must be pointed out here that this planet should be viewed just after the Sun has set. Some will tell you to observe it in the daytime. To do this with binoculars is dangerous. Venus is never far from the Sun and to sweep around the sky so near to it could result in the Sun entering into the field, causing eye damage.

There are scientifically useful observations which can be made with average binoculars. Variable stars can be watched as well as the occasional nova. By estimating their magnitudes at regular intervals work of value can be done. Possibly the best type of work for binoculars is the observation of brighter comets. If a comet has a sizeable tail then binoculars are likely to be the only way to see it properly.

There are some binoculars that are really special. Occasionally you may come across some which were built during the war. They will be large, very heavy and probably need a mount of some sort. One of the best known amateur astronomers, George Alcock, has a pair of 25 × 105s. They are real monsters. He uses them to search for novae and over the years has discovered three of these, plus four comets. Binoculars like these are a real rarity. If you are fortunate enough to come across such a pair you will probably not be fortunate enough to be able to afford them. However, small binoculars are very worthwhile and no observatory should be without a pair.

One of the major problems with binoculars in astro work is that for magnifications over 7× it becomes difficult to keep them steady, especially if using them for long periods. A good idea is to rest them on a fence or other suitable support. An up-turned brush has been suggested for this purpose but this can be a little awkward and uncomfortable. It is now possible to obtain fixtures with which binoculars can either be fastened to a G clamp or even on to a camera tripod. The latter is particularly useful, turning binoculars into an effective piece of equipment.

Figure 115. Ordinary binoculars secured with a commercially-available G clamp and tripod fixture to aid comfort and effectiveness for prolonged viewing sessions.

The telephoto lens as a telescope

Before finishing this section there is one small point worthy of mentioning. It is now possible to purchase an eyepiece which is made to fix on to certain types of telephoto lenses. The eyepiece turns the lens into an elbow telescope and also has a fixture for fastening the whole thing to a camera tripod. Obviously the instrument is not a powerful one, but a nice view can be obtained with a 300 or 400 mm lens. I would not suggest you purchase a telephoto for this purpose, but, if you already have one, the eyepiece is a useful little addition, even though a bit costly.

Even if you do not intend to use smaller equipment of this type for serious work, great pleasure can be had from its use. After using large telescopes and high powers it is sometimes very refreshing to look through equipment which gives nice bright low-power images and wide rich fields.

Figure 116. Commercially-available eyepieces made for attaching to telephoto lenses are fun to use. Although they do not make a powerful astronomical instrument, pleasant views of the Moon and rich star fields can be obtained.

Chapter 20

Telescope housings and observatories

Now that you are well fixed up with all the equipment likely to be needed for most types of amateur work, you are left with the problem of how to house the equipment, so it may be set up and left outside without weather conditions taking their toll. Housings can take many forms, but for the moment you only need to be concerned with two basic types. They can either be a cover for the telescope only, to be completely removed when the telescope is in use, or a full blown observatory building, which not only protects the telescope, but also the observer.

The run off shed

The simplest and most basic housing is really nothing more than a large box which slides away on short rails to expose the telescope. This could be a complete structure with a door at one end. If the telescope is a larger type making for a bigger cover then it could be designed so that it splits into two halves which slide away in different directions. (See Figures 117 and 118.)

The rails on which the 'run off shed' moves need only be lengths of angle iron fixed to long pieces of wood which have been sunk into a concrete base. Wheels are then fixed to the bottom frame of the covers. The whole thing coulld be made of plywood, or lengths of tongue and groove planking attached to a softwood frame. The overall structure will be so small that, even if made of quite strong wood, it will not be difficult to move. If the structure is coated with preservative then the roof covered with roofing felt, allowing for a slight overlap where the two halves meet, it will be surprisingly weather proof. Further small additions for convenience would be handles at each end for easier grip when moving the halves, plus hooks or bolts for fastening the two halves together when not in use. This will stop the wind from separating them.

Opening box type observatory

If the small run off shed is felt inadequate and something more substantial is required, this can still be done with relatively little cost, using basic materials. One type of design which has proved successful as a cover for my own 16½ in (419 mm) reflector, for many years, makes use of a large box, the

Figure 117. A run off shed in the closed position.

Figure 118. Inside view of one half of the run off shed showing the wheels and angle rail set in concrete.

top half of which opens back to reveal the telescope. The bottom half of the structure can be made of 3 in × 3 in (76 mm × 76 mm) heavy wood frame and floor boarding. The sturdier this half is the better. It should also have a small door to allow access.

The top half of the structure needs to be of much lighter material. Smaller 2 in × 2 in (50 mm × 50 mm) softwood framing should be used covered with corrugated plastic sheet, which is ideal and not too expensive. The back section of the cover needs to be strong, however. This should again be made from tongue and groove planking which is then hinged to the base section with three strong hinges.

The major problem with this design is that the top can be a little awkward to handle especially if on the large side. Opening can be assisted considerably by the addition of two large counterweights attached to each side of the upper half. If the weights are positioned in a particular way they will make the top easier to lift until it reaches the half-way point. Once past the halfway point they begin to act against it so that it does not fall back too heavily. To achieve this the weights will have to be fastened to the end of two long bars. These bars will then need to be fastened to the upper members of the top frame, roughly at the centre, and in such a way that they swing freely. Next, fasten a clip to the lower end of each side back member. When it is

Figure 119. A modification of the opening box type housing allowing opening of the upper section in two directions.

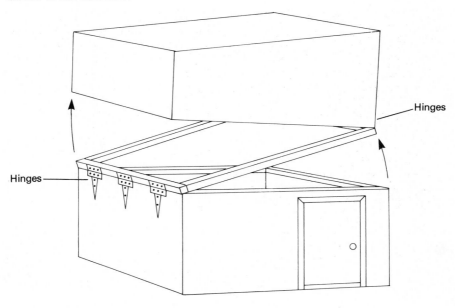

required to open the top, just swing the weights up toward the back and slip them into the retaining clips. The weights could be large cement-filled cans, allowed to set on to the ends of the long bars as described in chapter 17.

A further modification of this idea involves a novel way of making the upper section of the structure open in both directions. To do this the bottom frame of the opening section must be double. In other words when the upper section is completed make a second bottom frame in the manner of a spare. If one end of this spare frame is hinged to the upper portion of the structure and the other end hinged to the bottom base structure, the option of opening the roof section either way is afforded (see Figure 119).

With this type of design the roof need only be opened half way in each direction, which makes matters easier. By building two trestles to support it, when open it can be rested on these. While a totally unobstructed view of the whole sky is never allowed at one time, at least the whole sky is made available. The major problem with the idea is that when opened to the half-way point, the roof section is a fairly efficient wind trap. If used in high winds it might suffer damage. It could even blow shut causing injury to the observer. Some method of fixing it in the open position must be found, such as a wooden block used as a wedge.

Sliding roof

Another, particularly useful, idea makes use of a sliding roof. This design is best suited to refractors or Cassegrain reflectors which are, out of necessity, mounted on the top of a fairly high pedestal. Any instrument using a low mount with this type of building would be severely restricted in the amount of sky available to it.

A particularly ingenious mechanism is used to open the roof of Patrick Moore's observatory housing his 5 in (128 mm) refractor. The main building itself is just a large wooden-framed structure covered all over with corrugated plastic sheet, again quite easy to build and relatively cheap. The mechanism used to slide the roof back can only be described as inspired. It is due largely to a considerable amount of thought given to the problem by Reg Spry and despite its remarkable efficiency it is built from everyday materials.

The roof of the observatory is made to slide off in one complete piece. It runs on two pieces of ordinary angle iron, fastened to the top of the side walls, which act as a rail. A smooth running action is provided by three roller bearings fastened to each side member of the roof frame. Further ease of movement is afforded by another roller bearing fixed to the upper frame member of the back wall over which the roof slides. The centre frame member of the roof itself is made to run on this, having a steel strip fixed to its underside which runs on the bearing. Besides aiding the smooth running of the roof it stops any sagging.

The mechanism to make it slide is quite novel. Fixed to the upper beam of the back wall is a shaft running between small plumber block bearings. At

Figure 120. A sliding roof observatory open. The high walls of this type of housing allow its use only for telescopes mounted on tall piers, such as refractors or Cassegrain reflectors.

each end of the shaft, cycle sprockets engage two long loops of cycle chain running along the top of each side wall. These engage two further sprockets similarly attached to the front wall. The roof itself is fixed to the chains at points which are near to the front sprockets when closed. To make opening easier one of the back sprockets is double. This carries a further length of cycle chain which engages another (sixth) sprocket fixed lower down on the side wall with a crank handle. Turning the handle one way opens the roof, turning it the other way closes it. The sprocket and handle rotate on a shaft held in place by collars. The whole movement is very free. I know from personal experience that it has worked flawlessly for at least fifteen years.

The roof has to slide on to a frame fixed outside the back wall of the observatory. The angle rails obviously continue for the full length of the observatory side walls and frame. This frame could be fixed on to upright wooden supports or scaffolding as shown in the illustrations given here.

The dome

There are of course many types of observatory design ranging from ordinary huts with opening doors, to completely rotating sheds. All are very effective, easy to construct and cheap. There is however, one type of design which everyone associates with observatories, this of course being the dome.

Once the subject of dome building is considered, the problems at first seem insurmountable, and many give up the idea, opting for a more simple design. Domes are also horribly expensive to purchase, they are not some-

Above left *Figure 121. Domes can come to grief. This one, which the author was involved in the construction of, ended up on the ground after a strong gale. Always ensure that doors are secure and that no panels are likely to lift, allowing the wind to get into the dome.*

Above right *Figure 122. A small domed observatory housing an 8 in (20 cm) reflector. Detailed construction plans for this structure follow.*

thing many amateurs can even entertain, but it is possible to build your own dome with average materials provided you are prepared to give a little time.

I am not singing the praises of domes, far from it. In my time I have encountered many problems with them, having had one wrenched off its supports during a strong gale. This is not likely, however, so long as the dome is in one piece and closed. Should one of the panels lift, allowing the wind to get into the dome, then watch out, it will do a superb impression of a parachute. Also, thermal problems arise. The temperature inside the dome is usually not the same as that outside, this will result in air turbulence which will be most obvious in the vicinity of the opening. The air having different temperatures will meet here, causing a loss of image quality in the very area through which the telescope is to view. Neither problem is really serious and can be rectified. Just ensure the dome is in good repair and never use it during strong gales. Also try to remember to open the dome door some time in advance of an observing session to allow the temperature inside to level off.

Domes are great fun to build. One of the finest materials for this is hardboard which can be cut easily to the petal shapes required. Also it bends to shape over the dome frame. Provided it is well sealed it will last for years. The thing to watch for is any break in the protective skin of paint. If water is allowed to get to the hardboard it will soon rot. Great trouble will be saved if the structure is freshly painted each year before the onset of winter.

There follows a series of annotated diagrams showing how to construct the dome pictured in Figure 122. The particular plan is for a telescope in the range of 6-10 in (152-254 mm). It can of course be scaled up for larger instruments if necessary. The building shown has been in use for thirteen years and still works as good as new. It must be admitted that the comfort of using a telescope housed in such a way adds greatly to the pleasure of observing.

Domes do not have to follow the basic pattern. They can even be designed to fit in with garden surroundings. Figure 130 shows a rather attractive variation to the dome design which speaks for itself. The upper glazed half rotates, but because it is not true dome shaped, the shutters are easier to construct. The arrangement for rotating the top half can of course be similar to that shown previously.

Figure 123. Stage 1; (a) plan of the foundations, (b) section of the foundations.

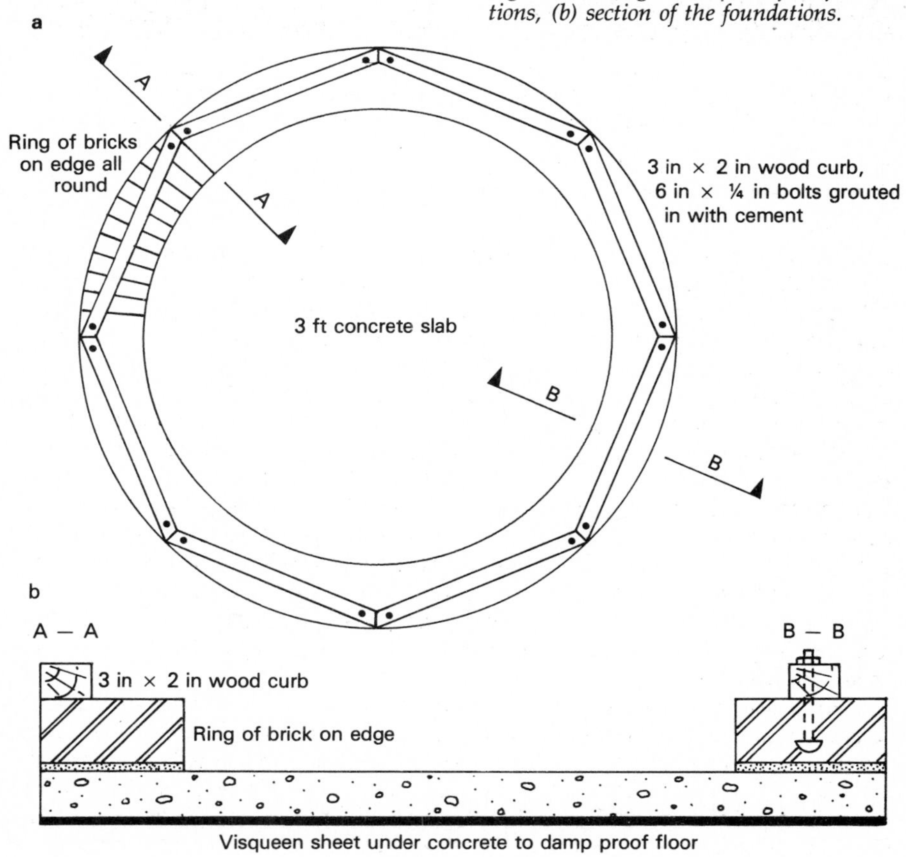

a

Ring of bricks on edge all round

3 in × 2 in wood curb, 6 in × ¼ in bolts grouted in with cement

3 ft concrete slab

b

A – A

B – B

3 in × 2 in wood curb

Ring of brick on edge

Visqueen sheet under concrete to damp proof floor

Figure 124. Stage 2; (a) walls of the observatory with the top curb, (b) plan of top curb from underside looking up.

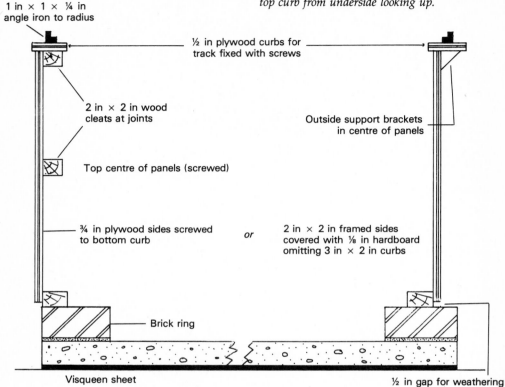

a

1 in × 1 × ¼ in
angle iron to radius

½ in plywood curbs for
track fixed with screws

2 in × 2 in wood
cleats at joints

Outside support brackets
in centre of panels

Top centre of panels (screwed)

¾ in plywood sides screwed
to bottom curb

or

2 in × 2 in framed sides
covered with ⅛ in hardboard
omitting 3 in × 2 in curbs

Brick ring

Visqueen sheet

½ in gap for weathering

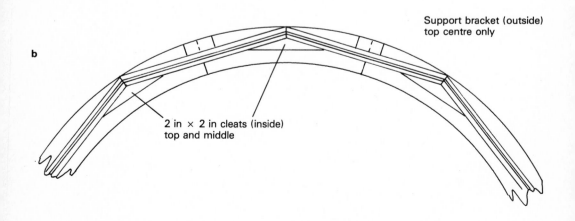

b

Support bracket (outside)
top centre only

2 in × 2 in cleats (inside)
top and middle

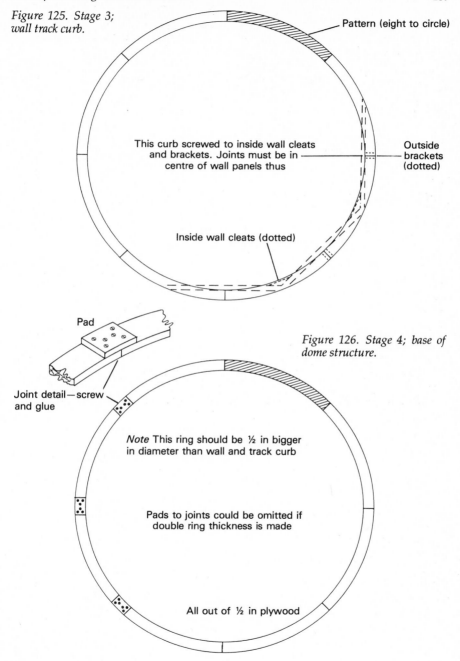

Figure 125. Stage 3; wall track curb.

Pattern (eight to circle)

This curb screwed to inside wall cleats and brackets. Joints must be in centre of wall panels thus

Outside brackets (dotted)

Inside wall cleats (dotted)

Pad

Joint detail—screw and glue

Figure 126. Stage 4; base of dome structure.

Note This ring should be ½ in bigger in diameter than wall and track curb

Pads to joints could be omitted if double ring thickness is made

All out of ½ in plywood

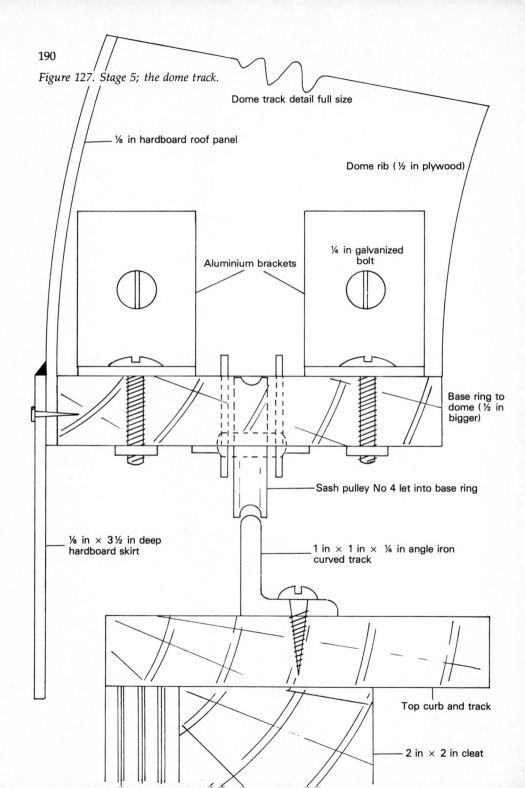

Figure 127. Stage 5; the dome track.

Dome track detail full size

⅛ in hardboard roof panel

Dome rib (½ in plywood)

¼ in galvanized bolt

Aluminium brackets

Base ring to dome (½ in bigger)

Sash pulley No 4 let into base ring

⅛ in × 3½ in deep hardboard skirt

1 in × 1 in × ¼ in angle iron curved track

Top curb and track

2 in × 2 in cleat

Figure 128. Stage 6; (a) plan of the dome and hatch, (b) side view of dome rib structure and hatch.

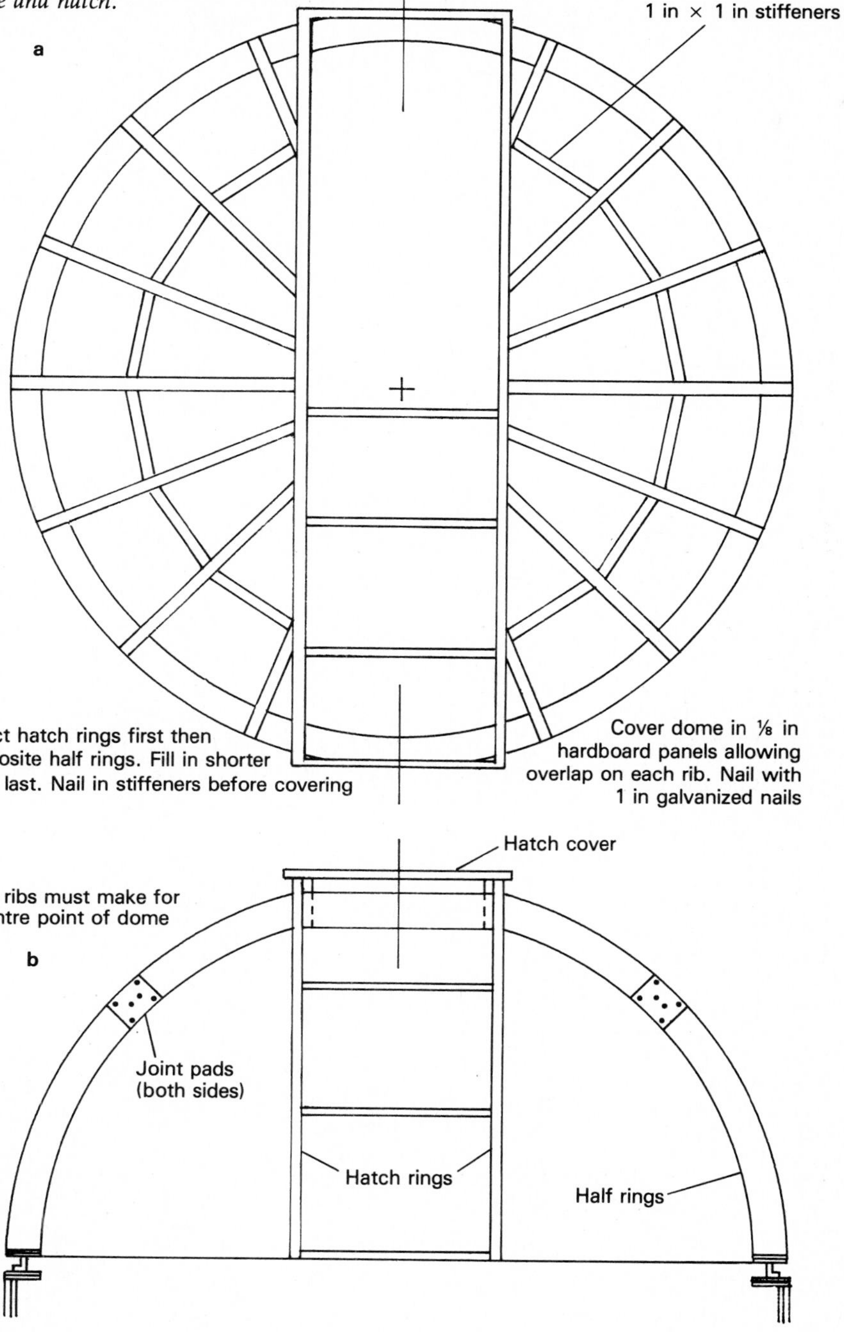

a

1 in × 1 in stiffeners

Erect hatch rings first then opposite half rings. Fill in shorter ribs last. Nail in stiffeners before covering

Cover dome in ⅛ in hardboard panels allowing overlap on each rib. Nail with 1 in galvanized nails

Hatch cover

All ribs must make for centre point of dome

b

Joint pads (both sides)

Hatch rings

Half rings

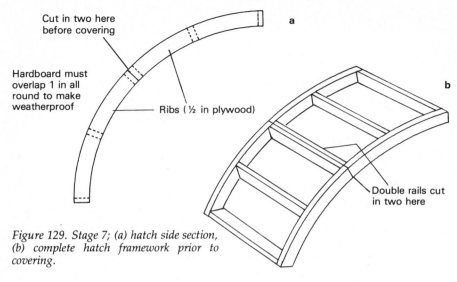

Cut in two here
before covering

Hardboard must
overlap 1 in all
round to make
weatherproof

Ribs (½ in plywood)

a

b

Double rails cut
in two here

Figure 129. Stage 7; (a) hatch side section, (b) complete hatch framework prior to covering.

Figure 130. Domes do not have to be of the conventional round shape. The design shown here would look well in any garden and is much simpler to construct than the spherical type.

Part Three

Chapter 21

Using the equipment

By now it is assumed that the choices have been made, some sort of observational equipment has been built or acquired and possibly some sort of observatory building set up. All that remains is to wait for the first clear sky and the true value of your equipment will be realized—or will it? Unfortunately the chances are that your first night's observing will in no way show the full potential of your telescope. There are many things, as you will soon come to realize, which the observer has to contend with.

Of primary importance is the ability to use the telescope, and this will only come with practice. It will be most evident when, after some months of use, a casual viewer is allowed to look through the telescope. This person will not see anything like the amount of detail on the planets, or the number of faint stars, seen by the seasoned observer. We describe this apprenticeship as 'learning to see'. There is no substitute for experience. The more observing you do the more experienced you will become.

Another problem all observers have to contend with is the gradual deterioration of eyesight with age, although this can, to a large extent, be countered by the gaining of experience. Apart from this, everyone's eyesight is different to start with, so some will obviously never see as much as others. Those who wear glasses must take this into consideration. In many cases removal of the glasses will improve matters when using a telescope even if they are needed for general use. If the exit pupil is small then any eye lens defect will not be so detrimental to the view, since only a small part of the eye lens is used. There are of course, certain eye defects that will require the glasses to be worn during observing in which case good eye relief will be essential.

Seeing conditions

More important than the observer's own eyesight and experience is the effect on the telescopic view by the atmosphere of the Earth. The day has finally arrived when astronomical observations can be made from above the atmosphere by satellites and telescopes placed in space. For these the atmosphere is no longer a problem. They can enjoy great clarity and observe in wavelengths not possible by Earth-based instruments. For the majority of us, however, whether amateur or professional, we are and will remain Earth based, therefore we will always have to contend with the resulting problems.

Most newcomers to astronomical observing assume that if the sky is cloudy no observing can be done, whereas if it is clear then everything is okay. It isn't quite that simple. True, if it is cloudy the situation for optical study is useless, however, if it is clear it does not mean that all is fine—not a bit, it can still be quite useless. Traces of the Earth's atmosphere extend many miles out into space. Even at a height of 60 miles (96 km) there is sufficient atmosphere to completely vaporize small particles of dust which enter the atmosphere at speed. Even so 90 per cent of our total atmosphere is found below 10 miles (16 km) with 50 per cent of the total mass below 3½ miles (5½ km).

It is this lower dense layer that gives the observer most trouble. The gases forming it are continually mixing and moving around, forever changing the optical properties of the air. It also contains a lot of water which will often be visible as cloud, but just because the sky is clear does not mean that there is any less water; all this means is that the water is present in the form of a gas and not actual water droplets such as cloud or mist.

Whatever the state of the atmosphere, poor seeing will always be less of a problem when observing parts of the sky higher than 50° altitude. The thickness of the layer through which the observation is being made is far less than when observing objects lower than 45°. This becomes worse still for objects near to the horizon. Even if seeing is good, rarely will objects lower than 15° be worth observing.

Bad seeing usually manifests itself in several ways. The worst conditions make observation pretty-well impossible—planetary images appear to shimmer and dance around and star images seem to jerk around rapidly. If the atmosphere is very agitated this movement will be so rapid that the star image will just be expanded to a large shimmering blob, possibly as much as 5 ″ to 10 ″ across, making resolution greater than this an impossibility. If you have a telescope capable of resolving down to a ¼ ″ then obviously the situation will be very frustrating. These sorts of conditions usually prevail following a depression in the apparently crystal clear sky of a cold front, though they can occur at any time. Seeing can become so bad that the images literally seem to boil, being in constant violent motion. Fortunately these occasions are quite rare, about as rare, in fact, as perfect seeing. The effect of this is even visible to the unaided eye. Scintillation, or twinkling of stars, particularly obvious on cold clear winter nights, results from conditions of poor seeing. The brilliant star Sirius will almost appear to flash on and off, even showing vivid colours when close to the horizon. This is chromatic scintillation resulting from its light being so dispersed that individual wavelengths are affected by turbulence independently of each other. On such occasions it will probably not be worth opening up the observatory.

On average nights only slight undulations of the image will occur and decent observations will then be possible. Now and then you will be treated to one of those rare nights when seeing is as near perfect as possible. All the waiting will have been worth while and maximum use should be made of the time. Visually, however, even the worst conditions can yield some results. The eye is capable of following the image under view as it moves around providing it moves around intact. Only when the image actually breaks up is the problem considerable. Even then there may be odd periods of fair seeing, fleeting moments when everything is steady. If you can train yourself to make the most of such moments, the number of totally useless nights will be reduced.

It is often said that telescopes of larger aperture suffer from poor seeing far more than telescopes of smaller aperture. This may appear to be so. Two observers viewing side by side with telescopes of different aperture will experience different apparent seeing conditions. The image through the larger telescope may be unobservable, while through the smaller instrument it may appear quite sharp. The larger aperture instrument is viewing through a wider cylinder of atmosphere and there is more air for turbulence to move around. Many observers actually stop down the aperture in an attempt to eliminate the problem. True, the image will appear sharper and clearer but in my view little is gained. Generally the ability of the telescope to see the effect of the conditions has been reduced because its resolving power is not now so great. Remember the section on resolution? If conditions are so poor that it is felt necessary to stop down you might as well cease observation until they improve, unless you are willing to wait for the odd good moment. If these moments do come along then your instrument at full aperture will be far more capable of making the best of them.

Localized conditions can also affect the view. The night may well be a good one but you will probably find certain objects indicate that the opposite is the case. It might be that a planet, or other object which you wish to observe, is approaching the rooftops of nearby buildings. Heat from these will cause seeing in that area to be poor and smoke from chimneys blowing or drifting across an object will have a similar effect. Heat from your own body can also cause problems, particularly with an open frame tube. Finally your breath, especially on very cold nights, can drift across the front of the telescope damaging image clarity. You will also notice that objects situated above trees or over open grassy areas will show better clarity. These are things you will become familiar with as you gain experience.

The amount of effect conditions have will depend on what you wish to do. If photography is to be attempted through a telescope with exposures of a second or more, then good results will be difficult to obtain in less than perfect seeing. The moving around of the image, which the eye can follow and the brain compensate for, will merely result in a fuzzy photographic image. Unless advantage can be taken of good moments, and this is far easier when using an SLR camera, photography, of the Moon and planets in particular, should only be attempted on very good nights.

Choice of object is also important as some are more affected by conditions than others. For this reason it is advisable to have a number of alternatives in mind. My own interests are in the planets and comets. Nights which are poor for planetary detail, because of atmospheric turbulence, might afford excellent transparency so that faint objects such as small comets will be detectable far more easily. On calm nights, with perhaps a mist and therefore poor transparency, the air can be perfectly steady, allowing the finest detail to be picked out on the bright Moon and planets. On such nights comets will be impossible to observe.

If the air is crystal clear, with no Moon, planetary images dancing all over the place and not a comet to be seen, why not try variable star work or even meteor watching. No clear night need be wasted if your interests are broadly spread.

Recording of observations and the Antoniadi scale of seeing

When any observation is made through the telescope, not only details of what is seen on the object under view should be recorded. Anything which is likely to have any bearing on the value of the observation should accompany any drawing or notes made. Obviously most important is the date and time of the observation. All observations should be accompanied by details of the type and size of the telescope used as well as the magnification employed. The location of the observer is also important, especially with timings of events such as occultations etc.

Most of the above is obvious. What many observers do not give, however, are full details of the seeing conditions experienced when the observation is being made. This can have a considerable effect on what is or is not seen. It enables those evaluating the observation to judge why one observer sees a particular thing while another does not. If both experience the same conditions of seeing then one or the other has to be suspect. If one has poor seeing while the other has good seeing, then, even if the same equipment is used, each observer would not be expected to see the same things. Proper recording of conditions, then, will add greatly to the value of the observation.

To make things easier, so that lengthy written details of the seeing conditions do not have to be given, causing unnecessary work for both observer and evaluator, a recognized scale of seeing has been devised. It was first used by E. M. Antoniadi, one of the greatest planetary observers of all time, and is now regularly used particularly by those involved in planetary work. Details are as follows:

I Perfect seeing with no quivering of the image.
II Slight undulations of the image with moments of calm lasting several seconds.
III Seeing moderate with some large air tremors.
IV Seeing troublesome with constant undulations of the image.

V Seeing particularly poor making the possibility of a rough sketch very difficult.

Other details required can also be abbreviated. The time of an observation should be given as Universal Time (UT). Telescope aperture should now be given in millimetres. If a reflector is used it should be written as either Spec or Refl, if a refractor it should be written OG. Finally magnification as × followed by the value. In this way all the required details can be given briefly, as shown in the following example for a hypothetical observation:

Date 1/3/86
Time 23.30 UT
Aperture and instrument 254 mm Refl
Magnification ×300
Seeing III (Antoniadi)

Obviously the Antoniadi scale is not of use with every type of observation. Those of comets, for instance, require different considerations. Transparency of the sky and presence of the Moon are of importance here so these must be mentioned. With regard to transparency an estimate of the limiting overhead magnitude of the stars should be given together with the phase of the Moon and estimated distance from the object under observation. If the Moon is absent from the sky at the time then this should also be mentioned, as should the presence of artificial lights.

In the case of meteor recording the percentage of cloud cover should be estimated since this will have a definite effect on the number of meteors seen. If an observer records twenty meteors in one hour with a perfectly clear sky, another observer at a different site will only record fifteen meteors if there is a 25 per cent cloud cover during the period of observation. The rate will of course remain the same for both observers and again evaluators of the results must have all the information to hand if they are to make sense of the information they are given. Any observers who do not give the full details of conditions must expect their work to be excluded from the rest, which would be an awful pity. The individual may well have worked hard and it may be the only observation for a particular period. A lot of damage will, therefore, be done by carelessness.

Chapter 22

Choice of object

Naturally the objects that you are likely to take an interest in will have a great bearing on the type of telescope you decide upon. Let us take a look at the various objects you may wish to observe and consider which instruments will be best suited.

The Sun

There are many areas of solar research which require specialist equipment beyond the scope of this book. Observations of the Sun in different wavelengths and of the solar prominences require expensive equipment, so this sort of work is not likely to be attempted by the raw beginner. There is, however, a fair amount of work which can be done with small telescopes. The observation of sunspots by projection is the main area of work for the amateur. For this a 2.5-3 in (63-76 mm) refractor or 4 in (102 mm) reflector will be quite sufficient. One of the best amateur solar observers, the late W. M. Baxter, used a 4 in (102 mm) refractor which is probably the best aperture for this type of work. With the Sun we have a different situation than with most other astronomical bodies—instead of not having enough light, we have too much. It is therefore inadvisable to use large equipment for projection because heat will cause damage.

Direct viewing, for most purposes, is not to be undertaken. There are filters advertised as being made specially for direct viewing but beware! Any filter for use at the eyepiece is to be avoided as it will, in all probability, splinter in the intense heat of the focused image of the Sun. This will leave the observer either with pieces of glass in his eye or damage caused to the retina by unobstructed sunlight falling on to it.

The only really adequate filters are full-aperture types which cut down the light and heat before it enters the telescope. Manufactured filters of this type can be expensive. Home-made filters are possible. These can be made by exposing large pieces of photographic film to full light and developing it. If two pieces are used together then light will be cut down to an acceptable level. The quality of this will not be so good as the manufactured filter, however. I am not suggesting these be used for direct viewing—projection is perfectly adequate here—only for photography. It is also advisable that an old camera body be used as the film holder, not an expensive new one, as damage will result should the filter become dislodged. It is for this reason that I do not recommend direct viewing even with supposedly safe filters, it is just not worth the risk. For photographs of the Sun guided telescopes will not be necessary. The image is so brilliant, even when filtered, that very fast exposures will be possible.

Sunspots are fascinating objects. They appear as an intense dark spot, or umbra, surrounded by a region which, though less dark, is usually more extensive and detailed. This is called the penumbra. The spots only appear dark by contrast with the brilliant photosphere. They are cooler than their surroundings but are still intensely hot. Umbral temperatures are around 4,000° K, penumbral around 5,500° K. They result from regions of intense magnetism which cause areas of activity when they erupt through the photosphere. Their range of size is enormous. They can be tiny individual spots around 500 miles (800 km) across or massive groups strung across a quarter of the Sun's disc.

Also seen are areas which appear slightly brighter than the surrounding photosphere called faculae. These regions are more elusive than sunspots. They are not usually seen against the bright photosphere at the centre of the solar disc but stand out quite clearly at the solar limbs where limb darkening increases contrast. It appears that they are active regions in the upper part of the photosphere. Though they commonly appear in the vicinity of active sunspot groups, they can appear on their own but usually signify that there is to be a fresh outbreak of spots. There are, however, odd occasions when they are seen outside the common latitudes of sunspots and are not associated with them.

Individual sunspots grow and decay in a few days. Large groups may last up to two months and be followed through two full rotations of the Sun. Actually the Sun does not rotate as a solid body. The equatorial region completes one rotation in around 25 days while the polar regions take nearer 35 days. It is thought that this differential rotation may result in the clearly established cycle of solar activity. Over a period of roughly 11 years spot activity will be seen to increase, reach a peak and then die down. At maximum activity the Sun will display a great number of spots, some even becoming large enough to be seen with the unaided eye if seen through fog or near to sunset. At minimum weeks may go by without a single spot being visible.

Generally the pattern is for the first odd spot of a new cycle to appear in fairly high latitudes both north and south of the equator. They are rarely seen above 40° latitude and never near the pole. The highest concentration appears in two belts at 30° N and S. As the cycle progresses toward its maximum, more and more spots are seen and the belts of concentration drift closer to the equator. At the height of activity—sunspot maximum—the latitude averages 15° N and S. Spots then gradually diminish in numbers but the drift toward the equator continues. They fade completely at around latitude 7° N and S.

Just before the spots of the old cycle die away, the first spots of the new cycle begin to form at higher latitudes giving a slight overlap. The spots of the new cycle have a polarity that is the reverse of the previous cycle. So, though visually the cycle seems to have an 11 year period, in reality it is 22 years. Adding to the overall complexity, the intensity of activity seems to change over a period of many years. There seems to be a much longer cycle superimposed on the shorter one. Also the 11 year period is only an average, sometimes the period is slightly longer, sometimes slightly shorter. Evidently there is a need for continual study, particularly in view of how important the Sun is to our existence here on Earth.

Apart from the actual observation of activity on the Sun itself, there are periods when the Moon passes in front of the Sun bringing about an eclipse. Total eclipses are quite rare but partial eclipses are common. When the latter occurs it is really of little scientific value but they do make for interesting photographs. Unfortunately from Britain we are going through a period when no solar eclipses are due for several years.

If an observer is fortunate enough to observe a total eclipse it will be the one time when the outer atmosphere of the Sun, or corona, will be clearly seen together with the odd prominence. For most of us a total solar eclipse is the only chance we get to see these. Unfortunately they are exeedingly rare for a given region and observers must be prepared to travel great distances to see one. It was for this reason that the portable 4 in reflector (102 mm), mentioned earlier, was originally built. Besides using this, however, perfectly acceptable photographs were obtained with only a 135 mm telephoto lens and tripod-mounted camera.

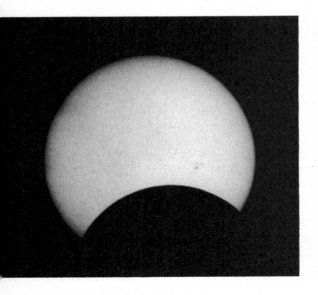

Figure 131. Solar eclipse. 29 April 1976. 10.10 UT. 3 in (7.6 cm) OG. Near maximum coverage.

The Moon

For the beginner the Moon is possibly the most exciting sight when viewed through a telescope. The amount of detail shown by even a small telescope is astounding. Ordinary binoculars will show many craters and mountains. Do not think that the best time to observe is when the Moon is full, however, most of the detail will be seen on that part of the Moon dividing the dark and light hemispheres, known as the terminator. The best time to view the Moon, therefore, is at half, gibbous or crescent phase.

Lunar craters range in size from a few feet to the largest of all—Bailly— which is 180 miles (289 km) across. Obviously the smallest are way beyond the greatest telescopes in the world. An idea of the detail that can be seen will be gained from knowing what is the smallest crater a given aperture will show, given in the following list.

Aperture		Theoretical limit	
in	mm	miles	km
2	50	2.5	4
4	102	1.3	2
6	152	0.8	1.2
8	203	0.6	1
10	254	0.5	0.8
12	304	0.4	0.6

The values given are the theoretical limits for each telescope assuming perfect conditions and optics.

Modest success is possible in lunar photography with little trouble as mentioned already, and the pleasure gained from securing your own pictures, whatever the quality, is great. Scientifically valuable work has been severely curtailed by the blitz of coverage the Moon received from the Americans during the lead up to manned landings, however there is still one area in which valuable work by the amateur may be possible. This concerns the observation of possible transient lunar phenomena, or TLPs. Certain parts of the Moon have, on occasions, been seen to exhibit strange glows, discolouration or obscuration. As the name implies, these are temporary in nature. They are thought by many to be evidence of active vulcanism or outgassing from beneath the lunar surface. This sort of event has been observed since the very early days of observation but it really became famous in 1958 when the Russian astronomer, Kosyrev, recorded a gaseous emission within the crater Alphonsus. This was the first occasion when spectroscopic evidence had been obtained and photographed with the result that such events began to be taken seriously. Since then numerous TLPs have been sighted, some being well confirmed.

Areas where this type of event seems most common are in or around craters which are situated at the margins of the Maria or lunar seas, Gassendi and Plato being such examples. Also Aristachus, the brightest lunar crater, has been the scene of such events. The most common appearance is a reddish or bluish glow. A recognized way of detecting these is to construct a Moon blink device. This is done by using two filters, one blue and one red. These, when placed in the filter holder described earlier, should be changed rapidly from one to the other and back again. If the glow is reddish it should be invisible with the red filter but dark when seen through the blue. This quick changing back and forth should make the region in question appear to blink on and off. Filters best suited are Kodak 25 red and 44A blue, the gelatine type being far cheaper than the glass.

Not all events display colour, so a thorough knowledge of the suspect areas is essential. Generally activity will last from a couple of minutes to around an hour, though some can last considerably longer. If an event is spotted, every attempt should be made to obtain confirmation. They should all be regarded with utmost suspicion in the first instance because it is very easy to be fooled. The ever changing angles of illumination can cause unusual effects. There are even some areas which display permanent colouration and which always show a blink when using the filters. Patches on the floor of Plato and Fracastorius tend to do this. Also, certain eyepieces suffering slight chromatic aberration will show a colouration to brilliant areas such as Aristachus. Always observe a suspect area with more than one eyepiece before reporting a TLP.

Another area in which the amateur can play a useful part is in the recording of occultations of stars by the Moon. Each month the Moon makes one complete circuit around the Earth. When viewed from the surface of the Earth it will be seen against a different part of the sky each night. During the night there is also a perceptible movement of the Moon against the background stars. Naturally many occasions will arise when it happens to pass directly over fairly bright stars. The path the Moon follows also varies within certain limits north and south of the ecliptic. The result is that a broad band of stars, centered on the ecliptic, stands a chance of being occulted by the Moon at some time or other.

If the stars are very bright then occultations can be spectacular, particularly if they disappear behind the dark hemisphere of the Moon. Even the brightest stars are so tiny that, with a couple of possible exceptions, they have no measurable size. At the moment of occultation, therefore, they snap out instantly. Most occultations are of fainter stars and the fainter the star the more difficult it is to see against the bright hemisphere. For stars of magnitude 6 or brighter moderate telescopes are fine and for the very bright stars a 2.5 in (63 mm) telescope or even binoculars will be sufficient. The brightest stars which can be occulted are Aldebaran in Taurus, Regulus in Leo, Spica in Virgo and Antares in Scorpius.

The idea is to time, as accurately as possible, the disappearance and reapparance of the star. Prior to full Moon stars will disappear behind the dark limb and reappear from behind the bright limb. After full Moon the opposite will be the case. Accurate timings from two or more locations can

Figure 132. Occultation of Venus by the Moon. 5 October 1980. 05.40 UT. 1/25 second. Primary focus 12 in (30 cm) refl. 400 ASA HP 5. Venus just reappeared from occultation. (A.W. Heath.)

give very accurate positions of the Moon and measures of the Earth's rotation period. For timings to be useful, the exact location of the observer must be known and the timepiece set accurately. A stop-watch should be used in connection with the speaking clock or with radio-broadcast time signals. Whichever, timings should be accurate to within one tenth of a second.

Although most stars blink out instantly, occasionally some stars have been seen to fade. Obviously, any such event should be noted. It indicates that the star may be a close binary system. Another interesting aspect of occultations is that at certain times and from certain locations the north or south limb of the Moon will be seen to graze a star. At these times the star will appear to wink in and out several times as it is occulted by mountains at the Moon's limb. This will give a profile of the Moon at that point as well as information on its motion.

Finally, every now and then the Moon will pass in front of one or other of the major planets. This can be a magnificent sight. It is wonderful to see Saturn with its rings or Jupiter and its four bright moons slide behind the limb of the Moon. Also, occultations of Venus during the daytime are a joy to see. Venus is bright enough to be seen in the daytime while the Moon might be virtually invisible, so the planet will seem to vanish into thin air.

The planets

There are nine major planets. Five are bright, easy naked-eye objects, three are telescopic objects, the other is of course the Earth. Venus and Mercury orbit the Sun closer in than the Earth and so are referred to as inferior planets. The rest orbit the Sun at greater distances than Earth so are called the superior planets. Each has a fascination of its own and is worthy of individual description.

Mercury

Because this planet is so close to the Sun, its mean distance being 36 million miles (58 million km), it never appears far from the Sun. It is never seen in a dark sky, only in the twilight before sunrise or after sunset. At such times it is quite low in the sky so it is is not seen clearly because of poor atmospheric conditions. To see it properly it should really be observed when high in the sky during the hours of daylight. Contrast will be low but seeing better.

Mercury is only a small planet. Its diameter is just over 3,000 miles (4,878 km). From Earth it presents a disc ranging from 5" to 13" across. Because it orbits the Sun inside the Earth's orbit it is seen to go through the full range of phases. When on the far side of the Sun, at superior conjunction, its disc is small and full. When on the near side, at inferior conjunction, it is at its largest but we see only its unilluminated hemisphere. The best time for observation is around greatest elongation. It is then at its greatest angular distance from the Sun which can be anything from 18° to 27°. When actually standing at greatest elongation the planet presents a half phase. This may be either east or west of the Sun depending on whether it is approaching or receding from Earth. Mercury's orbital period is only 88 days so it is continually catching up with and passing the Earth.

Because of the difficulties of observation moderate aperture telescopes are required to see it well. Do not expect to see any detail with telescopes smaller than 6 in (152 mm). Markings on the planet are very faint appearing only as dusky patches on a pinkish grey disk. To see markings at all clearly requires apertures of 10 in (254 mm) or greater. We now know that Mercury has a heavily-cratered surface. We can never hope to compete with spacecraft photographs we have received and therefore Earth-based study of the surface is of little value. It is, however, very pleasing to pick out this elusive little world and in view of all the difficulties you can congratulate yourself if you obtain a clear view.

There is one type of observation which can be carried out successfully with small telescopes. Each time Mercury passes through inferior conjunction it is situated between the Earth and the Sun. The planet's orbit is fairly highly inclined to the plane of the Earth's orbit, in fact its inclination to the ecliptic is 7°. The result is that more often than not, as seen from Earth, it will pass some way north or south of the Sun at each conjunction. There are times when inferior conjunction occurs at a time when Mercury is at one or other of its nodes, which is at present around 7 May or 9 November. At such

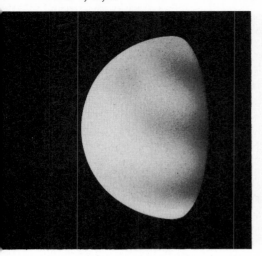

Figure 133. Drawing of Mercury. 2 April 1977. 16.30 UT. 16½ in (42 cm) refl ×248 and ×372. Seeing II (Antoniadi).

Figure 134. Drawing of Venus. 30 May 1985. 11.24 UT. 5 in (12.5 cm) OG ×250. Seeing II (Antoniadi).

times Mercury will transit across the Sun's disc. When these occur the disc of Mercury will be around its maximum angular size so it appears as a clear round black disc against the brilliant Sun.

Observation of transits should be made by the projection method as with sunspots. Mercury will appear rounder and blacker than the spots themselves and will cross the disc far more quickly. A full central transit will last for about 8½ hours. If the transit occurs at sunspot minimum, as the last one did in 1973, there will be no trouble in picking it out. A 2 in (50 mm) refractor will be sufficient to show it. Unfortunately transits are rather rare. The last two occurred in 1970 and 1973. Fortunately we are fast approaching the next, due on 13 November 1986.

Venus
Whereas Mercury is elusive, Venus is anything but. Apart from the Moon and Sun it presents the most conspicuous object in the sky. It is so brilliant that it can cast shadows if conditions are right. Its magnitude may reach as high as −4.5 when at its greatest brilliancy. It is an inferior planet like Mercury, going through the full range of phases for the same reason. Its size range is greater because it can approach closer to and move further away from the Earth.

Venus has a diameter of 7,700 miles (12,320 km) which is just a little smaller than the Earth. At superior conjunction it presents a full disc just over 10″ across. At inferior conjunction it may reach 63″ in angular diameter. The best time for observation is the intermediate periods when the disc ranges between 15″ and 50″. At greatest elongation, when the phase is exactly half, it may be as far as 47° from the Sun and visible up to 4 hours after sunset or before sunrise.

It may come as a surprise, at first, to learn that, despite being so conspicuous, the disc of the planet is all but featureless. Venus is shrouded by a dense atmosphere filled with sulphurous clouds. These are highly reflective which make the planet so brilliant but all that is ever seen in the way of markings are faint dusky patches, the occasional light area and a brightening of the cusps of the planet. Generally the features are of such low contrast that if observed against a dark sky the brilliancy of the planet swamps them out. For this reason serious observers prefer to observe during daylight hours. In fact it is possible for keen-sighted people to pick it out during the day without optical aid, provided they know just where to look.

We now know that the drift rate of the clouds yields an atmospheric rotation of 4 days, even though the solid body of the planet completes one rotation in 243 days. To see the faint markings more clearly filters, using the filter holder described earlier, should be used. Kodak Wratten 15 yellow, 25 red, 58 green and 47B blue are recommended. Telescopes larger than 3 in (76 mm) aperture together with a little experience are needed to see the features. If over 6 in (152 mm) for a reflector and 4 in (102 mm) for a refractor, so much the better. 10×50 binoculars will show the phase of the planet when half or crescent. Again, I am not suggesting that you go sweeping around the daytime sky close to the Sun with binoculars. The chances of pointing them toward the Sun is too great, please wait until the Sun has just set.

One type of observation that is quite worthwhile is one that has to be carried out when the sky is quite dark with Venus presenting a narrow crescent. Occasionally it has been reported that the dark hemisphere shows a faint ghost-like glow referred to as ashen light. The true reason for this is still a bit of a mystery. It has been suggested that aurorae on Venus are responsible but since the planet has a very weak magnetic field it is difficult to imagine how they could be powerful enough to be detectable from Earth. Venus has a strange atmosphere with powerful electrical storms. Active vulcanism is also believed to exist there so there could be many reasons for this phenomenon. A continual watch for the effect will help in finding an explanation for it.

Mars

This is the first planet encountered outside the orbit of the Earth. At 4,169 miles (6,794 km) it is a little over half the diameter of the Earth. Most of the time it is at such a distance from Earth that because of its small size observation is difficult. When at opposition, which occurs on average every 780 days, it approaches quite close to the Earth. At these times it is seen on the opposite side of the sky to the Sun, well placed for observation. The apparent size varies greatly from 3.5″ when on the far side of the Sun to 26″

Figure 135. Drawing of Mars. 14 April 1982. 21.40 UT. 16½ in (42 cm) refl ×372. Seeing I (Antoniadi).

at the most favourable oppositions. Some oppositions are not so close, however, because Mars has a rather eccentric orbit. Closest approaches bring it to within 35 million miles (55 million km) but at some oppositions it may be 63 million miles (99 million km) away with a diameter of only 14″.

Even at best, favourable observing periods are rarely more than 2½ to 3 months each side of opposition. For regular useful work an 8 in (203 mm) reflector or 5 in (128 mm) refractor is necessary. We are seeing the actual surface of the planet in the case of Mars. Markings take the form of bluish grey, greenish or brownish patches on a reddish background. Bright pink and even whitish regions are also evident, which together with the glistening white polar caps make for a very colourful object.

Spacecraft have been into orbit and have soft-landed on Mars so we know a great deal about its topography. General observation of the surface markings, therefore, now only serves to familiarize the observer with the features. Some dark markings are not consistent, however, occasionally they may fade or rise to prominence. New markings may sometimes appear, only to disappear again after a few months or even years. Spacecraft have not remained in the vicinity of Mars to study this sort of thing as yet so in this area there is room for Earth-based study. Because of its 24.62 hour rotation period, markings seen at a certain time on a given night will be presented in the same position half an hour later on the following night. This is very convenient for checking anything unusual.

It is also possible to observe clouds on Mars. Prominent ones are rare but worth watching for. Occasionally dust storms break out causing localized obscuration of the regular features. Sometimes these may be of such proportions that the surface of the whole planet becomes obscured. This is another area where Earth-based study is of value.

Mars has two small moons, Phobos and Deimos. Both are very small and quite faint as seen from Earth. Quite large telescopes are required to see them easily. I have never seen them with my 16½ in (419 mm) and feel that at least an 18 in (456 mm) reflector and possibly larger is required to even glimpse them.

Jupiter

Even for the amateur with only a small telescope, Jupiter presents a most exciting sight. It is the largest planet in the Solar System, having an equatorial diameter of 88,700 miles (142,800 km). Though at opposition it can never come closer to us than 367 million miles (590 million km) it presents a disc with an angular diameter of 47". A magnification of 40× is all that is needed to give it an apparent size equal to that of the full Moon when seen without a telescope. Even when on the far side of the Sun, at conjunction, and standing 600 million miles (960 million km) away it never presents an angular diameter less than 30".

Because of its size the disc is visible almost as soon as magnification is applied. A pair of 7×50 binoculars will show it, while detail on the disc will be picked out with 2.5-3 in (63-76 mm) refractors or a 4 in (102 mm) reflector. Useful work on the planet is possible with a 6 in (152 mm) reflector. With 10-12 in (254-304 mm) reflectors, on occasions, there will be so much detail seen that it will be difficult to record it all.

Jupiter is one of the type of planets known as the gas giants. Unlike the smaller inner or terrestrial planets, Jupiter has no solid surface as such. It probably has a small solid rocky core about the size of the Earth surrounded by a sphere of solid metallic hydrogen approximately 60,000 miles (100,000 km) in diameter. Closer to the surface where the pressure becomes less, the hydrogen assumes a liquid form. So the metallic hydrogen sphere is probably covered by a 12,500 mile (20,000 km) deep ocean of liquid hydrogen. Closer still to the surface, at a depth of about 620 miles (1,000 km) the hydrogen assumes its gaseous state. It is the upper layers of this atmosphere that we see; a region of hydrogen and helium gas which has high altitude clouds of ammonia ice crystals, beneath which are dark reddish brown clouds containing crystals of ammonium hydrosulphide, dense layers of water mist and abundant amounts of methane.

Though the largest planet, Jupiter has the shortest period of rotation of all the planets, completing one revolution around its axis in less than 10 hours. The surface we see does not all rotate at the same rate. Basically there are two rates of rotation; a broad central zone around the equator, System I, which has an average period of 9 hours 50 minutes 30 seconds and the tropical, temperate and polar regions, System II, with an average rotation period of 9 hours 55 minutes 40 seconds. Within each of these regions there are various currents which result in many different rotation periods for different latitudes.

Because of its incredible distance from the Sun it receives relatively little heat. In fact the planet itself radiates far more heat than it receives. This results in tremendous convection currents which are set up within the gases of the atmosphere. Large individual convection cells are drawn out by the rapid rotation to form bright and dark bands in the planet's visible atmosphere. The bright bands are called zones, here warm air is rising. The dark bands are called belts, here cooler air is sinking. The zones appear to be at a much higher level than the belts and it seems that in the darker regions we are seeing far deeper into Jupiter's atmospheric layers. Apart from the large scale features there are many smaller individual convection cells, circulatory systems and general regions of turbulence which give a highly detailed appearance to the planet.

Jupiter's most famous feature is a large reddish-coloured oval known as the Great Red Spot. Apart from the general belt structure there is nothing about the visible features that is of a permanent nature. Spots come and go, some in days, some in weeks, some even last for years, but sooner or later they fade away. The fame of the Great Red Spot is not only its size and colour but the fact that it seems to have persisted at least for as long as observational equipment has been capable of showing it, which is over 300 years. It is a mystery how such a feature could last so long. Recent spacecraft images show it to be a massive circulatory feature completing one rotation

Below left *Figure 136. Drawing of Jupiter. 23 February 1980. 23.40 UT. 16½ in (42 cm) refl ×248. Seeing III-IV (Antoniadi). Red Spot and hollow on central meridian.*

Below right *Figure 137. Drawing of Jupiter. 7 April 1980. 20.42 UT. 16½ in (42 cm) refl ×248. Seeing IV (Antoniadi). Note the double shadow transit—these are the shadows of Satellite I (larger) and Satellite II (smaller). Satellite II itself has just moved off the disc to the left.*

around its own centre each 11 days. The spot itself is situated in a curious white hollow. Every so often the spot will fade, the hollow, however, remains. When the spot returns to prominence it reappears within this hollow.

The main type of useful work in connection with Jupiter is to time features across the central meridian of the planet. If the feature is large, time its leading end, centre and following end. Such timings tell us about the currents and turmoil within the atmosphere of Jupiter. We can learn of the life history of thousands of features if enough observers are prepared to give their time.

Jupiter has sixteen moons, most of which are too faint to be seen from Earth. Four of these are very bright. These are the Galilean satellites Io, Europa, Ganymede and Callisto. All four are easily visible with 7×50 binoculars and they would be visible to the unaided eye were they not so close to Jupiter's brilliant image.

For anyone with a moderate telescope these moons offer a great deal. Large telescopes do show some detail on their discs but the Voyager spacecraft during their encounters with Jupiter in 1979 returned remarkably detailed photographs of each satellite so nothing of value can be done in this direction. However, during their orbits they regularly pass in front of and behind the planet. Jupiter's axial tilt is only 3° to the plane of the ecliptic which means that only the outermost, Callisto, will pass north or south of the disc at certain times during Jupiter's 12 year revolution period around the Sun. As a result there are four phenomena that are regularly visible. Satellites may be either occulted by Jupiter or eclipsed by its shadow, they may themselves pass in transit across the planet's disc or cast their shadows on to it. Also, every six years, the plane of the satellites' orbits pass through the Sun and Earth. At these times, mutual phenomena occur. Satellites may occult or eclipse each other. Timings of all these events are useful and in any case they are a joy to watch.

Saturn

What Jupiter offers in detail, Saturn offers in beauty. It is a planet similar in many ways to Jupiter and is also a gas giant. Its upper atmosphere is marked with belts and zones and it has a rapid spin, which, because of the planet's low density, makes it bulge at the equator even more markedly than Jupiter. Saturn's equatorial diameter is 75,160 miles (120,000 km). Its rotation period at the equator is 10 hours 14 minutes, while at the poles it is 10 hours and 39 minutes.

Saturn's distance from the Sun averages 886,100,000 miles (1,427 million km). Despite this it presents a respectable-sized image. The angular size of its globe ranges between 14", when at conjunction, to 21" when at its most favourable opposition. Therefore at an average opposition a magnification of 100× will give an image similar in size to the full Moon as seen with the unaided eye.

Detail on Saturn's globe is far less clearly defined than detail on Jupiter. The disc is fairly bland with only the occasional outbreak of spot activity. These may be dark spots or condensations in the belts or bright ovals in the zones. Because of their relative rarity they are very important when they do occur. Until we have orbital spacecraft around Saturn the value of Earth-based study will remain. In fact since the Voyager missions it has become of

Below *Figure 138. Drawing of Saturn with rings open (tilt 15°). 2 June 1983. 21.36 UT. 15 in (38 cm) refl ×360. Seeing II (Antoniadi). The ring's north face is presented to us which will not be the case again until 1995.*

Bottom *Figure 139. Drawing of Saturn with rings edge on. 18 February 1980. 00.31 UT. 16½ in (42 cm) refl ×248. Seeing II (Antoniadi). At the time the drawing was made the unilluminated north face of the rings was just visible, Rhea and its shadow were just entering on to the disc and Tethys was just about to enter into the shadow of Saturn's globe (left).*

greater value because we can now combine information from both sources, thus gaining a better understanding of the planet.

The most famous of all disturbances ever seen on Saturn was a great white oval on the equatorial zone in 1933. This was discovered by none other than Will Hay who, apart from being a famous comedian, was a well-known amateur astronomer. The subsequent observations of this spot told us much about the currents existing within the equatorial zone. There have been other important spot outbreaks but unfortunately, owing to the lack of observers interested in this type of observation, many an opportunity has been missed. The same method of observation used on Jupiter also applies with Saturn. Timings of features across the central meridian should be made whenever possible. For this type of work reflectors of at least 8 in (203 mm) aperture will be necessary.

The beauty of Saturn results not from the ball of the planet, but from the magnificent system of rings which surround it. The size of this sytem is pretty impressive. The rings have an overall diameter of 170,000 miles (272,000 km) and an angular size at average opposition distance of 45″. The tilt of Saturn's axis to its orbital plane is 26.7°. This means that during its 29½ year period of revolution around the Sun the rings are presented at various angles to the Earth's line of sight, which can be anything from edge on to a tilt of just over 26°. Actual edgewise-on rings occur after 13½ and 16 year periods. The shorter period has the southern face of the rings on show, the longer period has the north face presented to us. The rings are no more than a few kilometres thick and are invisible from Earth when exactly edge on. When at their widest opening the ellipse of the rings may be seen with only 10×50 binoculars. To see them well a telescope of at least 3 in (76 mm) aperture will be needed.

There are three major components of the rings; the outer two, ring A and B, are bright and separated by a narrow division called the Cassini Division. Inside the two bright components is the fainter Ring C. This cannot be seen with telescopes smaller than 6-8 in (152-203 mm). Cassini's Division may just be seen with a 3 in (76 mm) telescope when the rings are at their widest opening.

Saturn has a large family of satellites, numbering 23 in all. Only nine were known prior to the Voyager encounters. Many are too faint to be seen from Earth but at least five are visible through moderate instruments and two with small telescopes. The brightest of all is Titan, Saturn's largest moon. This may be seen with only a 2 in (50 mm) refractor. Rhea is just about visible with a 3 in (76 mm) instrument. The other three bright moons Iapetus, Dione and Tethys require a 6 in (152 mm) to see them easily.

Occasionally eclipses, occultations, transits and shadow transits of Saturn's satellites are visible but these can only happen at times when the planes of the satellite orbits pass through the Sun and the Earth. The satellites are generally in the same plane as the rings, the most notable exception being Iapetus. These events will only be seen for a couple of years either side of edgewise-on rings. Events concerning Titan are the most obvious and these may be seen with a 3 in (76 mm) telescope.

The outer planets

All of the outer planets need the use of some sort of telescopic equipment to see them well. In fact all were discovered by the use of the telescope. Uranus was discovered in 1781 by W. Herschel, Neptune in 1846 by J. G. Galle and Pluto in 1930 by C. W. Tombaugh.

Uranus

This planet is just visible to the unaided eye, having a magnitude of 5.7. Binoculars will show it well but its greenish 3.5" disc needs a fairly large telescope and a magnification of 450× to give it a size similar to the unmagnified image of the Moon. I have only been able to make reasonable observations of it with reflectors over 15 in (381 mm) and refractors over 12 in (304 mm) though this has not been helped by the fact that since 1966 the planet has been situated south of the equator. What detail can be seen on the disc is always highly suspect. Faint belts and patches have been reported with instruments of 10 in (254 mm) aperture. Most of the time Uranus' pole is

Below left *Figure 140. Drawing of Uranus. 10 June 1980. 23.00 UT. 15 in (38 cm) refl ×350. Seeing II-III (Antoniadi). The dark hemisphere is the polar region of Uranus entering into the sunlight after many years in darkness. The bright limb is the receding equatorial region.*

Below right *Figure 141. Uranus and three of its satellites; Umbriel (upper), Oberon (middle) and Titania (lower). 16 May 1980. 00.30 UT. 16½ in (42 cm) refl ×372. Seeing II (Antoniadi).*

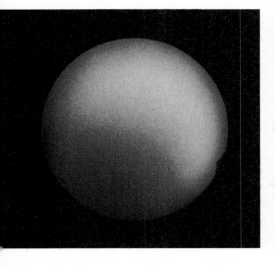

directed toward us. Its axial tilt of 98° means that it is virtually lying on its side and so presents a fairly featureless fuzzy greenish disc.

Uranus has fifteen satellites, but only five were known before the Voyager 2 fly-by in January 1986. Of the previously-known satellites, the innermost, Miranda, is too faint to be seen visually and was discovered by photography with a large telescope. The remaining ones can all be seen visually. Ariel requires at least an aperture of 18 in (457 mm), but I have glimpsed Umbriel with a 16½ in (419 mm). The outer two satellites, Titania and Oberon, have been claimed to have been seen with a 6 in (152 mm) though I have found them exceedingly difficult with a 10 in (254 mm), only being satisfied completely that they were there with a 15 in (381 mm).

After the January 1986 encounter with the planet by Voyager, most Earth-based observational work is now obsolete. There is still one thing which can be done and strangely enough small telescopes are all that is required. The results do not concern Uranus itself but the Sun. The idea is to carefully estimate the magnitude of the planet. To do this properly Uranus must only show as a near pinpoint image, so very low magnification is required. Estimates are made by comparison with nearby stars of known magnitude. The planet's magnitude will of course vary as its distance from us varies, however, in the past it has shown changes in brightness that have not been attributable to the regular reasons. It has been suggested that these variations are a result of brightness changes in the Sun itself. The Sun is so bright that small changes would probably not be detectable easily. Because the planets reflect sunlight back to us, they might indicate any changes in the Sun by changes in their own brightness. The faint Uranus happens to be the best candidate for this type of work.

Uranus is now known to have a faint system of rings. Though they are not visible in the normal way from Earth we have received evidence of their existence when the planet has occulted certain stars. Any such occultation should be observed with great care. Occultations of reasonably bright stars are rare and fainter stars will require reasonable-sized telescopes if they are to be followed easily. When such an event does occur, careful note should be made of any variation in the star's brightness, both before and after occultation by the planet itself.

Neptune
This planet does present a real problem, even for the professional. Information so far gathered about it is very poor. It is another gas giant which, like Uranus, is about four times larger than the Earth. The visual magnitude is only 7.8 so it cannot be seen without optical aid. Binoculars will just show it but to see its 2.3" bluish white disc at a size resembling that of the unmagnified Moon a large telescope and a magnification of 700× will be needed. Virtually no detail has ever been seen on the disc, at best dusky patches and perhaps a dusky equatorial band have been detected. Hopefully Voyager 2 will send back detailed pictures during its August 1989 encounter with the

Figure 142. Neptune and its brighter satellite Triton. Two drawings made on 6 June 1980 at 23.15 UT and 7 June 1980 at 23.45 UT, both with a 15 in (38 cm) reflector ×360 in good seeing conditions considering the low altitude of the planet from the British Isles at the time of observation. Note how the position of Triton with respect to Neptune has changed over a 24-hour period.

planet. Until then we cannot expect to learn much about this distant world.

Neptune has two known satellites with some recent observations indicating a third. Only the largest, Triton, is easily visible with moderate telescopes. It is just about within the range of an 8 in (203 mm) reflector, though a 12 in (304 mm) is required to see it well.

Pluto

This is a rather faint object having a present magnitude of just under 13.8. It should be visible with anything over an 8 in (203 mm) reflector. Again to see it clearly large instruments are essential. Pluto's orbit is quite eccentric, its distance from the Sun varies greatly. We are lucky enough, at present, to be passing through a period when the planet is at perihelion, that is at its closest approach to the Sun. In fact, during the period 1979 to 1999, Pluto is closer to us than Neptune. When at the most distant part of its orbit, as it will be in the year 2114, its magnitude will be below 16 so large telescopes will be needed to show it.

Having an angular diameter of only 0.2" means that its disc is difficult to resolve even with the world's largest telescopes. No detail whatsoever can be seen on it. Recently, professional astronomers have proved Pluto to be a double planet. Its companion, known as Charon, is around 500 miles (800 km) in diameter and Pluto itself is only 1,500 miles (2,500 km) across.

The only useful work to be done is to observe Pluto on the rare occasions when it occults a star. If the star is bright enough, then even if Pluto itself is not visible its effect on the star as it cuts out its light will be.

Figure 143. Pluto as observed with a 16½ in (42 cm) reflector × 248 on 14 April 1977 at 21.45 UT and 15 April 1977 at 22.40 UT. The magnitude of the planet was estimated at 13.8 and was seen quite easily with this instrument.

Smaller bodies of the Solar System

Besides the planets there are other bodies in the Solar System which will repay study. Meteors have already been covered in the section referring to cameras and photography but there are two other types of object which can be easily followed with small or modest equipment. Most interesting are the comets. These are tiny bodies which wander around the Solar System with highly elliptical orbits, only becoming visible at those times when they approach the parts of their orbits near to the Sun. The solid part of the comet, called the nucleus, is a mixture of rock and ice probably at most a few kilometres across. At great distances from the Sun a comet remains inactive, but, as it closes in on the Sun, heat starts to evaporate materials in the comet's nucleus and a cloud of glowing gas and dust (called a coma) forms around it. When even closer to the Sun this gas and dust is repelled by solar radiation pressure to form the comet's tail.

With large comets the head and tail can be spectacular, however most are small and faint. On average we can expect at least one comet visible with the naked eye per year, with a fairly spectacular one each decade. Great comets are rare. There have been only two this century, these being the Daylight Comet of 1910—often confused with Halley's Comet of the same year—and West's Comet of 1975-76. There are many different types of instrument which can give useful results in the field of cometary observation. Large comets can be very extensive, occasionally stretching across a considerable

Right *Figure 144. Comet West 1975n photographed by the author on 9 March 1976 using an ordinary camera with an f3.5 135 mm telephoto lens and FP 4 film. The camera was mounted 'piggy-back style' on a portable telescope and hand guided on the comet for 15 minutes. Bright comets like this one are rare but when they do occur ordinary cameras are one of the best ways to capture their beauty.*

Below *Figure 145. Comet Iras Araki Alcock 1983d photographed by the author on 11 May 1983. In this case the comet was only a little over three million miles from Earth—the second closest recorded approach of a comet—and moving very quickly. It presented a very large diffuse image without a tail. The photograph was taken using an ordinary standard 50 mm lens at f2 and the film was FP 4. Three exposures were made, each 3 minutes long, then the three negatives were sandwiched together for the print. The time period between each exposure was 10 minutes and 5 minutes respectively. The amount the comet had moved during these periods is indicated by the displacement of the star images. The two bright stars to the left are Dubhe (upper) and Merak (lower) of Ursa Major and are known as the pointers.*

amount of sky, so binoculars and even the naked eye are important ways of gathering information. Large comets do, however, display small scale phenomena which may require larger telescopes to see them properly. These are important because they may have some effect on the whole comet's appearance at a later date. It is fair to say then that a full range of equipment can be useful in one way or another.

Most comets are very small and need some form of optical aid to render them visible at all, but even a telescope of around 4 in (102 mm) can be expected to allow useful observation of six or more comets each year. Rich-field telescopes giving a bright image, wide field of view and low magnification are best suited. Estimates of the size of the coma, degree of its condensation and total magnitude (the latter of which is obtained by comparing the comet's image with nearby out-of-focus star images) are all of value. Information gathered will help us to find out how each comet acts as it approaches toward and recedes from the Sun. Any visible detail within the coma should be noted, as should details in and position angle of any tail seen. Photography is particularly useful. Long guided exposures will show detail in the tail not seen visually, but at the same time they will burn out the image of the head through over exposure so losing detail there. Visual observation, therefore, must always accompany photographic work.

Perhaps the most useful work the amateur can do is to discover new comets. Though professionals discover a large number most are not actually looking for them at the time. Some amateurs do go out of their way to find them and many are quite successful. A low power and wide field plus a great deal of patience are required. Generally comets are picked up after 300 hours' search time, though of course this varies considerably. Should you discover one your name will be given to it provided the discovery is verified and you are among at least the first three people to spot it independently.

The other minor bodies of the Solar system are the asteroids or minor planets. Many of these are bright enough to be seen with small telescopes and one, Vesta, reaches naked-eye visibility. The most useful work is to estimate their magnitude. Variations will indicate if the body is irregular in shape and yield its rotation period. Lately, the observation of stellar occultations by asteroids has proved valuable. By use of these we have been able to accurately determine the shape and size of certain asteroids. Occasionally during an occultation the star has been seen to disappear twice indicating that the asteroid passing in front of it is double. Asteroids are numerous and the chances of occultation quite common. Anyone with telescopes ranging from 3 in (76 mm) upwards can do this type of work though obviously larger instruments will offer more opportunities.

The stars
Once we leave the realm of the Solar System we enter a field where the professionals are deeply involved. Very few amateurs are in a position to compete with the sophisticated equipment they use, so the bulk of the work

Above left *Figure 146. Drawing of Comet Halley as seen on 3 December 1985 at 17.40 UT with a 10 in (25 cm) reflector and a magnification of 36.*

Above right *Figure 147. Minor planet 433 Eros photographed on 21 January 1975 at 00.10 UT. The photograph was taken using a 135 mm telephoto lens at f3.5 with a 12 minute exposure on FP 4. The bright star at the centre is Pollux and to the upper right is Castor. Eros is indicated by an arrow.*

must be left to them. There is one area, concerning the variable stars and their explosive relatives the novae, where the amateur can be useful. Many stars do not shine with a steady light, but are seen to vary in brightness. Some of these brightness fluctuations are very minor but some are quite drastic. There are thousands of these stars which vary in brightness, most of which fit into several groups. A high percentage are quite bright when near maximum light and within easy reach of small telescopes, binoculars or even the naked eye. What follows is a very brief list of some of the more common types.

Eclipsing binaries
This is a large group of variables in which the apparent change in brightness is not actually a change in the star itself but occurs because they are stars which form a close pair orbiting around each other. Binary systems, triple and multiple systems are common. Because the stars are too close to be separated visually, they always appear as a single star. When they are out of line their combined light gives the brightness maxima. When one star eclipses the other the total light drops giving the brightness minima. By estimating the brightness at regular intervals a light curve can be constructed.

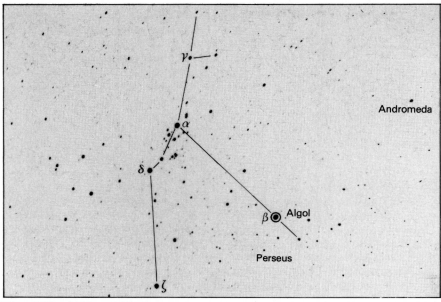

Figure 148. Position of Algol.

Figure 149. Position of Beta Lyræ.

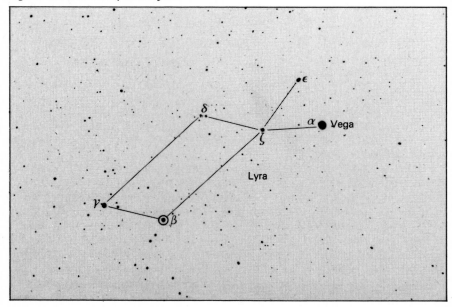

From this we can learn about individual components of the system.

The most famous examples of this type are the naked eye stars Algol (β Persei) which has a magnitude range from 2.2 to 3.5 over a period of 2.8 days and β Lyrae with a magnitude ranging from 3.4 to 4.3 over a 12.9 day period. The light curve of the latter indicates that the two stars are elliptical in shape due to tidal forces resulting from their close proximity to each other. Also it is known that a stream of high temperature gas is flowing from the primary to the secondary, some of which is spiralling out into space.

Pulsating variables
Another large group of variables. The light variations in these cases result from changes within the star itself. Some change with very regular periods, whilst others show no pattern at all.

Cepheids and RR Lyrae stars
Cepheid variables are the most famous class of pulsating stars. There are two main types known as the classical Cepheids and the Population II Cepheids or W Virginis stars. Cepheids are supergiant yellow stars with periods from one to a hundred days. They have turned out to be particularly useful in the measurement of astronomical distances because of a convenient period luminosity law. The brighter the mean absolute magnitude of the star the longer the period. Once the period of a Cepheid is known its actual luminosity is automatically known so we were able to estimate its distance from its apparent brightness. It is generally believed that the variations occur because of an expansion and contraction of the star's outer layers. The most famous example of this type is δ Cephei which is one of the brightest stars of this group, as well as the first to be discovered. It varies between 3.78 and 4.63 magnitude over a period of 5.3 days.

There is another group known as the RR Lyrae stars which are largely found in globular clusters. All are faint and have periods of less than a day. They are different in that their variations cease for a time, only to begin again as before.

Long period variables
All of this type are red giant or supergiant stars. They have periods which range from 100 to 700 days, and though they do have a rough period this is nowhere near as regular as the Cepheids. Their overall magnitude variation is generally very large; many of the best known reach binocular or even naked-eye brightness when at maximum, but they become invisible in all but quite large telescopes when at minimum. The total change in brightness may be as much as 100,000 times in some cases, though in other wavelengths than visible light the different is not so great.

The most famous of this class are Mira (o Ceti) and χ Cygni. Mira is a truly spectacular variable. It normally spends periods of 5 to 6 months near mini-

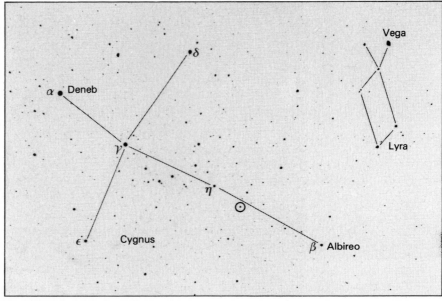

Figure 150. Chi Cygni; (above) maximum, (below) minimum.

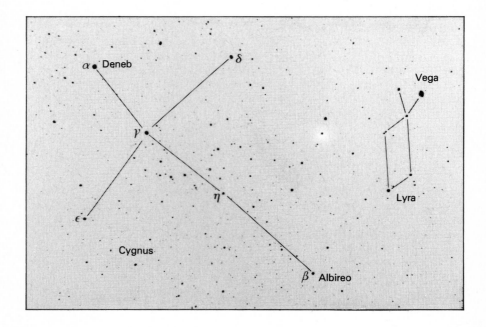

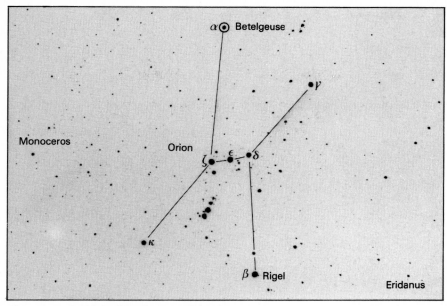

Figure 151. Position of Betelgeuse (Alpha Orionis).

Figure 152. Position of Gamma Cassiopeia.

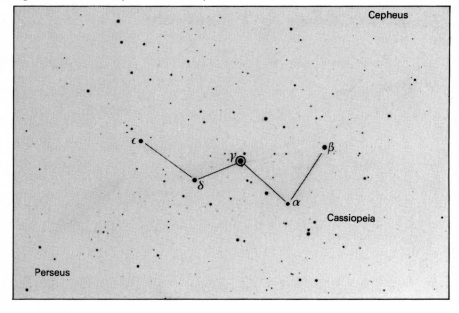

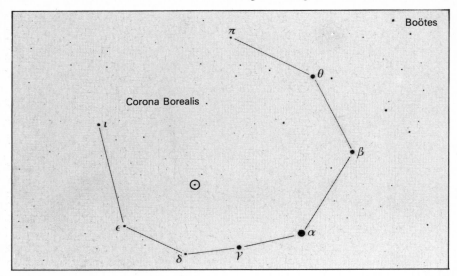

Figure 153. Position of R Coronæ Borealis.

mum with a magnitude of between 8.5 and 9.6. It will then rise to a maximum becoming visible to the naked eye for a few months. Each maximum is different, being anything from magnitude 2 to magnitude 5. Occasionally it has been reported to reach first magnitude, however. Chi Cygni is also spectacular. It ranges from 2.3 to 14.3 magnitude over a period of 400 days.

Semi-regular variables

Again these are all red stars. Their variation in magnitude is far less than with the long period types. They usually have an amplitude not greater than two magnitudes. Some have three or four periods of different length superimposed upon each other making for a very complex light curve. The most famous of the class are α Herculis which has a magnitude range of between 3.0 and 4.0, and Betelgeuse (α Orionis) which usually varies between 0.4 and 1.0 magnitude.

Irregular variables

These are stars which have no trace of a period, and whose magnitude variations are small. The best known examples are γ Cassiopeiae, which varies between 1.6 and 3.3 magnitude, and μ Cephei which varies between 3.6 and 5.1 magnitude.

*   *   *

There are many other types of variable which are less common. Most are

Figure 154. Nova Cygni 1975. The photograph above was taken two nights after maximum brightness when the nova had already faded by nearly two magnitudes to 3.5. The photograph below was taken eleven days later on 12 September when the Nova had faded well below naked eye visibility to magnitude 7.2. Another feature of this nova was the striking change in colour from bluish white, just prior to maximum, to yellowish white, around and shortly after maximum, then finally a strong red a week after maximum. The bright star lower right is Deneb (Alpha Cygni).

faint but perhaps the best known oddity is the peculiar star R Coronae Borealis. Most of the time this star is just about visible to the unaided eye with a magnitude of around 5.8. Suddenly it will drop, sometimes by only one magnitude to 7.0, sometimes down to as low as 14.0. There then follows a slower climb back to maximum which is marked by many minor fluctuations.

Novae

It is in this field of stellar astronomy that the amateur can play a vital part. Again large telescopes are not necessary for it is not in the actual study of novae that we are concerned here, but in their discovery. Highly specialized equipment is required to study these objects and this is best left to the professional. His problem, however, is that we never know just when one is going to appear. It is therefore not possible for him to spend the time looking for them. This is where the amateur with a good knowledge of the sky can help. Novae can appear any time, anywhere so it is better if a number of observers choose a set region of the sky and adhere to it. The pattern of stars in the region chosen should be learned by heart so that with experience memory of the star patterns will improve and any new star will be spotted. Again small rich-field telescopes or very good large-aperture binoculars are ideal for this. When a discovery is made it should be reported as quickly as possible following confirmation so that professionals can begin to study it.

Deep sky objects

Most of the work the amateur can do regarding the nebulae, clusters and galaxies is to a great extent for pure enjoyment only. To photograph them long guided exposures are necessary. Some deep sky objects are visible to the unaided eye, the best examples being the Pleiades open cluster, the Globular Cluster M13 in Hercules, the Andromeda Galaxy, M31, and M42, the Orion Nebula. Binoculars will show many more. The most famous list of such objects is the Messier catalogue compiled by Charles Messier in 1784. Obviously there are more complete catalogues now but for amateurs there is always a desire to try to see all the objects in Messier's list. It gives a good cross-section of the brighter examples including some bright planetary nebulae. A great deal of fun can be obtained by searching for them and a 4 in 6102 mm) reflector will show them all quite well. Some of the brighter objects can be photographed with an ordinary camera using a telephoto lens. Good results can be obtained with only a 135 mm lens.

Again, though most scientific work must be left to the professionals, there is one area where the amateur can be of value. One class of object not so far discussed are supernovae. These are stars which literally collapse, blowing off their outer layers. In so doing their brightness suddenly increases many millions of times perhaps over as little as a few hours. They are exceptionally rare. Only three have been seen in our Galaxy since records began. These were in 1054, 1572 and 1604. There is no way of knowing when the next will

Above left *Figure 155. Drawing of the Whirpool Galaxy (M51) made with a 15 in (38 cm) reflector. The spiral structure of this galaxy can be seen with instruments down to 8 in (20 cm) aperture.*

Above right *Figure 156. Photograph of the Andromeda Galaxy (M31) taken with an ordinary camera using a 135 mm f3.5 telephoto lens. The exposure was hand guided for 15 minutes and the film used was FP 4.*

Below *Figure 157. The edgewise spiral galaxy NGC4565 in Coma Berenices, as seen with a 15 in (38 cm) reflector. The object is 15 minutes of arc by 1 minute of arc in size so it is a fine object with even a 6 in (15 cm) reflector.*

occur. One could occur tomorrow or it may be centuries before we see another. When they do happen they are so bright that they outshine all other stars in the Galaxy and can be easily seen during the day. Unfortunately, no supernova has been seen in this Galaxy since the invention of the telescope. All our information about them has been obtained from supernovae seen in other galaxies.

There are hundreds of thousands of galaxies scattered throughout the Universe. Many of these are within the reach of amateur telescopes. Even if an individual galaxy suffers only one supernova each 200 years then a study of 200 galaxies will yield a possible outburst every year. Again a continual systematic study is the way to succeed. There are some, more advanced, amateurs who carry out a photographic patrol of a certain number of galaxies, but success can just as easily come through visual study. Each galaxy needs only to be examined for a few minutes every clear night. In this way a fair number can be covered during an observing spell of an hour or two. Look out for any faint star you have not previously noticed. With practice you will soon be able to recognize the pattern of the few stars around each galaxy, spotting any newcomer should it appear. Fortunately, most easily visible galaxies lie in parts of the sky well away from the Milky Way, so star numbers around these are pretty low making the job easier. Often, when a supernova does appear, it has a magnitude greater than the total magnitude of the whole galaxy to which it belongs. So if you can see the galaxy you will have no difficulty in seeing the supernova when it occurs.

This work is of exceptional value to the professional. Our knowledge of the supernova mechanism is still pretty poor. Until the day that a supernova occurs in our Galaxy we must be satisfied with the study of those elsewhere.

*   *   *

That just about covers everything of general interest which can be studied with your home observatory equipment. There is certainly much to do. As we have seen, astronomy is one area in which amateurs can play a useful role. If you wish to take part in serious observational programmes then it is advisable to join a recognized society which has within it sections set aside for study of specific objects. The British Astronomical Association and the Association of Lunar and Planetary Observers in America have such sections for observers.

Even if being useful does not appeal to you then it cannot be denied that a great deal of pure pleasure is easily obtained by just looking at and enjoying all of the many interesting things in the sky that a telescope will show. This in itself is often sufficient to make many wish to take a closer look. The telescope is our way of leaving this planet. In a single night it is possible to cover vast distances; to see and appreciate things that our ancestors could never have understood or even believed possible. Anyone interested should get a telescope and take advantage of the opportunity it affords in showing the wonders of the Universe around us.

Bibliography

Amateur Astronomer's Handbook, J. B. Sidgwick, revised by James Muirden, Pelham Books 1979.

Constructing an Astronomical Telescope, G. Matthewson, Blackie & Son Ltd 1958.

Eyes on the Universe—The History of the Telescope, Isaac Asimov, Andre Deutsch Ltd 1976.

Standard Handbook of Telescope Making, N. E. Howard, Harper and Row 1984.

Make your own Telescope, R. Spry, Sidgwick & Jackson 1978.

Exploring the Night Sky with Binoculars, P. Moore, Cambridge University Press 1986.

Norton's Star Atlas, A. P. Norton, Gall & Inglis Ltd.

Observational Astronomy for Amateurs, J. B. Sidgwick, Pelham 1982.

The Amateur Astronomer and his Telescope, Gunter D. Roth, Faber & Faber 1972.

The Astronomical Telescope, B. V. Barlow, Wykeham Publications 1975.

The Great Palomar Telescope, Helen Wright, Faber & Faber 1951.

Using the Telescope, J. Hedley Robinson, David & Charles 1978.

Amateur Telescope Making—Books 1,2 & 3, Albert G. Ingalls (Editor), Scientific American Incorporated 1981.

Sky and Telescope Magazine, Sky Publishing Co.

Index